care and
Repair of your
Large
Home Appliances

by Ernest Tricomi

EDITORS and ENGINEERS, LTD.
New Augusta, Indiana

FIRST EDITION

FIRST PRINTING — JUNE, 1965

CARE AND REPAIR OF YOUR
LARGE HOME APPLIANCES

Copyright © 1965 by Editors and Engineers, Ltd., New Augusta, Indiana. Printed in the United States of America.

Reproduction or use, without express permission, of editorial or pictorial content, in any manner, is prohibited. No patent liability is assumed with respect to the use of the information contained herein. While every precaution has been taken in the preparation of this book, no warranty is made and Editors and Engineers, Ltd. expressly disclaims any liability for results of the use hereof, liability being assumed by the user hereof.

Library of Congress Catalog Card Number: 65-21513

PREFACE

If any one thing characterizes the modern home, it is the sixty-cycle hum of electric motors working quietly in almost every room in the house. One motor pumps refrigerant through a tall, insulated cabinet designed to keep food fresh and palatable for days and weeks. Another motor strokes an agitator, deep in suds, to wash clothes sparkling clean. Still another tumbles the clothes in a stream of warm air, which is also furnished by electrical current, to dry them quicker than even the warmest summer day can.

All this machinery requires careful operation and a minimum amount of maintenance if it is to continue to give uninterrupted service. The homeowner who is gifted with some mechanical aptitude will discover, on reading this book, that he will be able to keep the "home fires burning" in the majority of cases of mechanical and electrical failures. In the case of a serious failure or a major replacement, the services of a capable technician should be sought.

The theory, functioning, electrical characteristics, and major components of four typical major appliances are covered in this book. Each type of major home appliance is similar to all others of the same general type in nearly all respects. Thus here the emphasis is on learning the how's and why's of an appliance so that the reader with some degree of mechanical and electrical know-how can answer for himself how to make detailed repairs and servicing.

Whenever one detail of functioning in a particular make or model differs from that found in others, it has been explained and described. No attempt has been made to give step-by-step disassembly, since this is largely a matter of common sense.

By the intelligent use of this book, many hours of delay in obtaining a serviceman for minor repairs can be eliminated, and many dollars of expense can be saved.

Ernest Tricomi

CONTENTS

CHAPTER 1

GENERAL INFORMATION 7
Electrical Terms and Definitions—Safety Precautions—Test Equipment—Electrical Testing—Preventive Maintenance—Electric Motors Used in Home Appliances—Performance Checks

CHAPTER 2

REFRIGERATORS AND FREEZERS 25
How a Refrigerator Works—Defrosting—Refrigerator/Freezer Combinations—Electrical System—Performance Checks—Common Refrigerator and Freezer Repairs—Troubleshooting Guide

CHAPTER 3

WASHING MACHINES 49
Tumbler Washers—Agitator Washers—Automatic Washers—Conventional Washers—Mechanical Systems—The Water System—The Electrical System—Performance Checks—Troubleshooting Guide

CHAPTER 4

CLOTHES DRYERS 79
Gas Dryers—Electric Dryers—Troubleshooting Guide

CHAPTER 1

GENERAL INFORMATION

Major home appliances need electricity, if not as the major source of energy, at least as a secondary one to provide light for control panels, to drive motors, and to run clocks. Even the automatic gas water heater, with no visible connection to house current, uses a weak, self-generated current flow to hold open a gas solenoid valve. It is important, then, for you to have a good understanding of the properties of electricity, as well as its application in the home.

Electricity is available in two distinct types—alternating current and direct current. When direct current is used, it is found in commercial and industrial establishments and has no application in the appliances discussed in this book.

To gain a better understanding of the electrical components in appliances, you should have a speaking acquaintance with electrical terms. Most introductions to electricity draw a comparison between electricity flowing through a wire and water flowing through a pipe. This discussion will be no exception, for this is an excellent way of illustrating the behavior of electricity. Just remember, though, that electricity flows with lightning speed through its "pipes."

ELECTRICAL TERMS AND DEFINITIONS

Voltage is a measure of electromotive force, or pressure, without regard to flow; it can be compared to the pressure of water, whether it is moving or standing, in a pipe. Voltage is measured by a voltmeter.

Amperage, or current, is the rate at which electrical current flows through a conductor; it can be compared to gallons per minute of water flow through a pipe. The unit of current measurement is the ampere, and it is measured by an ammeter.

Resistance is the opposition a conductor offers to the flow of an electrical current. This opposition in a conductor may be compared to pipes of small and large diameter. The small-diameter pipe restricts the rate of flow (small-diameter wire has a higher resistance). A large-diameter pipe would permit more gallons of water to flow past a given point per minute (large-diameter wire has a lower resistance). The unit of resistance is the ohm, measured by an ohmmeter.

Wattage is the power required to do work. Electrical power is measured in watts and can be related to horsepower measurements of mechanical force, i.e., 1 horsepower is equal to 746 watts. In simple terms, power in watts is the product of volts times amperes. Power is measured by a wattmeter.

Cycles per second is a measure of the *frequency* at which ac changes direction. All communities in the United States have 60-cycle ac, meaning that the current changes direction 120 times each second (twice each cycle). In some countries supplies are 50 cycles per second.

Fusing

Fuses are used to protect the house wiring system and the appliance from overloads and short circuits. Fuses usually consist of a strip of metal which melts at a relatively low temperature. When the fuse is intact, current flows through the metal just as it would through any good conductor. If a sudden surge of current (high amperage) occurs, due to a short circuit or an overload, the accelerated rate of flow of electricity through the narrow strip of metal will generate enough heat to melt it, thus breaking the current.

In some appliances, notably garbage disposers, a momentary overload is normal during the time necessary for the drive motor to gain momentum. In these cases, a thermal-delay fuse (*Fusetron*, etc.) is used. This type of fuse will tolerate an overload for a short period, but it will open instantly if a short circuit develops.

Fuses are of the screw-in or plug type (Fig. 1-1A), or the cartridge type (Fig. 1-1B). Usually plug fuses are

(A) Screw-in type. *(B) Cartridge type.*

Fig. 1-1. Two types of house fuses.

used in 120-volt lines, while cartridge fuses may be used in 240-volt and higher power lines. Both are rated in amperes, indicating the maximum amount of current the metal strip or internal element will carry without melting (blowing). Plug fuses are rated up to 30 amperes, while cartridge fuses may be rated from 3 amperes to as high as 600 amperes.

Circuit Breakers

Another means of protecting a line is with a circuit breaker, most of which employ an electromagnet which breaks the circuit when its magnetic field is intensified to the maximum allowance. Having broken the circuit, the device is prevented from reclosing by the force of a spring. Thus, circuit breakers must be reset manually, even if the cause of the overload is corrected. If, when the device is reset, the overload condition persists, the circuit breaker will again open the circuit immediately.

Grounding

Electricity, like water, follows the path of least resistance. Suppose that the insulation has worn off and a bare wire touches the exterior metal cabinet of an appliance. If the cabinet is properly grounded, the electricity will find an easy path to the ground through the ground wire, which is connected to a cold-water pipe. Any lesser conductor of electricity (such as a human body) which may also touch the cabinet at the same time, will have no current flow through it, since it offers more resistance than the ground wire. If no other path to ground exists, however, then the electricity will flow through the body, with sometimes disastrous results.

Those appliances which should be grounded, such as washers, dryers, dishwashers, air conditioners, and ranges, are always accompanied by complete grounding instructions and kits. Do not defeat the purpose of these grounds by avoiding them—they are installed to protect against fatal shocks and demand very careful installation.

SAFETY PRECAUTIONS

The first rule when working with electricity is to disconnect the appliance from the outlet and remove the fuse, or open the circuit breaker, at the control box. Even this rule is not completely foolproof, however, because the wrong fuse might be removed. Therefore, after disconnecting the circuit, test by turning the appliance "ON" to make doubly certain that the line is dead.

Personal safety is a vital consideration both of yourself as you work on the appliance, and of the subsequent user. Connections should be secure so that they will not work loose with vibration or normal use. Never rely on the terminal screw or the electrical cord to support weight or strain of any kind.

If screws and other minor components are replaced, make sure they are of the right size. A longer screw or a bulkier component might penetrate the insulation of a wire, causing a short to the cabinet.

If new branch lines must be installed, they should be installed by a licensed electrician. Branch lines in the home are usually run with solid metal conduits (called thin-wall) with wires drawn through them, but may be either armored cable (BX) or a nonmetallic sheath cable (Romex), as shown in Fig. 1-2.

Never replace a 15-amp fuse with a 20-amp. This is asking for trouble, because a circuit bearing a 15-amp fuse is most likely not intended to carry 20 amperes. On the other hand, when replacing electrical components in

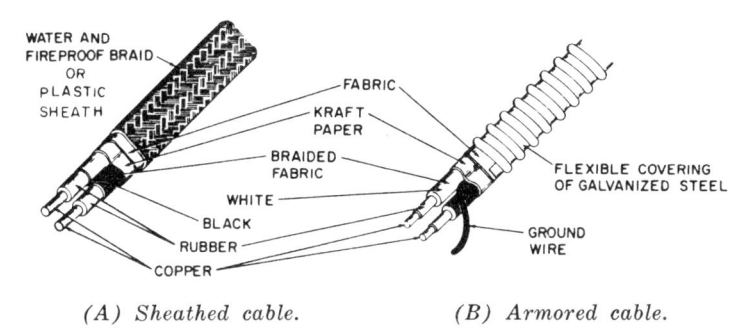

(A) Sheathed cable. *(B) Armored cable.*
Fig. 1-2. Types of house-wiring cables.

the appliance itself, never replace with a component of *lesser* value of capacity. The same is true of wiring—if part of the wire harness of an appliance must be replaced, be sure the replacement wire is the same size as the original.

TEST EQUIPMENT

Test equipment can be of considerable aid in diagnosing the cause of trouble in an appliance. Generally speaking, the purpose of testing is to discover whether or not current is flowing through a particular component without opposition or leaks. Thus, components may be found to be "leaky" or "open." The procedure is to disconnect the component from the regular line, connect the leads from the test equipment to the component terminals, then plug in or switch on the test equipment to get a reading on the dial. Following are a list and description of some useful items to test equipment that you may need.

Bell Ringer

This homemade testing instrument consists of a pair of dry-cell batteries and a bell or buzzer connected as shown in the illustration (Fig. 1-3). It is called a *continuity tester*. Since the bell will ring when the leads are touched to each other, it follows that when the leads are touched to opposite ends of a continuous circuit, the bell or buzzer will sound if the circuit is unbroken, and will not sound if the circuit is broken.

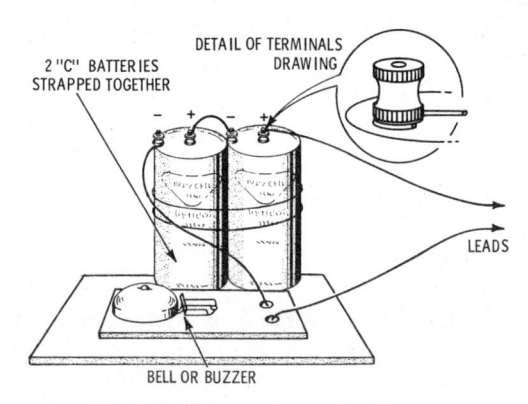

Fig. 1-3. Homemade continuity tester.

By testing smaller and smaller segments of a broken circuit, the break can be located, whether it is in a segment of wire, or a particular component of a system.

Testing for ground is also accomplished with the same instrument by touching one of its leads to the metal frame of an appliance, and then touching the other lead to one of the appliance terminals. If the bell or buzzer sounds, there is a ground and the condition must be located and remedied before operation of the appliance is allowed.

Series Test Lamp

The test lamp uses household electricity, instead of dry cell batteries, as its source of power. You can make your own by purchasing an ordinary lamp socket, a wall plug, a pair of wire clips, and a length of wire from an electrical supply store. Assemble the components as shown in Fig. 1-4.

When the test leads are brought into contact with each other, and the instrument is plugged into a wall outlet, the lamp will light. In order to check for a broken (open) circuit, follow this procedure:

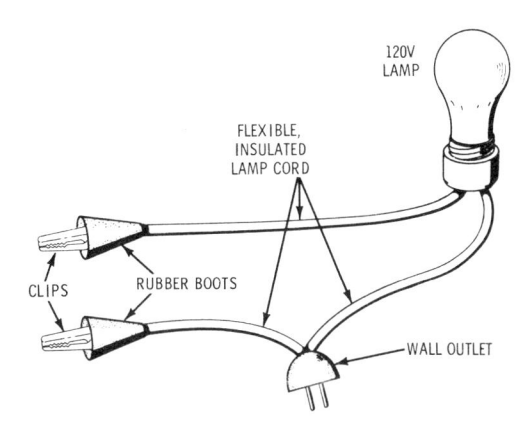

Fig. 1-4. Homemade series test lamp.

Attach the test leads to the terminals on the plug of the component or appliance you are testing. Be sure to remove your hands or any other part of your body from contact with the appliance. Plug the tester into the wall outlet briefly. **(IMPORTANT: Never plug the tester into the outlet before attaching the test leads.)** If the lamp goes on, the circuit is unbroken (closed); if the lamp fails to go on, a defective (open) circuit is indicated. Be sure the appliance switch is "on" in this test.

A grounded circuit is indicated if the lamp lights when the test leads are connected to the metal frame of the appliance and one of its terminals, and the tester is plugged into the power source. Try this test between each plug terminal and the metal frame.

Professional Test Equipment

The following pieces of test equipment are used by technicians, not only to determine power breaks, but to analyze the appliance for defects such as leaky motor capacitors, excessive friction in mechanical trains, or excessively low source voltage. The home repairman will normally find such equipment beyond his abilities, but a short discussion of each instrument may be helpful in understanding some of the failures that electrical appliances are subject to.

Ohmmeter—These serve chiefly to test electrical continuity in order to locate shorts or breaks in circuits, segments of circuits, switches, thermostats, and start capacitors on motors. An ohmmeter ordinarily measures resistance; when applied between points where continuity is supposed to exist and no meter indication is obtained, the circuit is open and the component being checked should be repaired or replaced. If the needle moves, the circuit is closed and can be considered functional (this does not apply to motor capacitors).

Ammeter—A hook-on ammeter (Fig. 1-5) is a convenient test instrument because it does not require disturbing the circuit to obtain a reading. Ammeters are used for measuring current flow, the reading being compared with a standard established by the appliance manufacturer.

Voltmeter—This is a necessary tool for determining high- or low-voltage conditions which may contribute to unsatisfactory performance. It can be used to measure voltage at an outlet or, by disconnecting a motor and substituting a voltmeter, the amount of voltage being delivered by the appliance wiring harness to the motor can be measured.

Wattmeter—A wattmeter helps the service technician determine how efficiently the mechanical system of an appliance is functioning. Too low readings can indicate weak or worn-out components in a circuit. Too high readings can indicate mechanical friction.

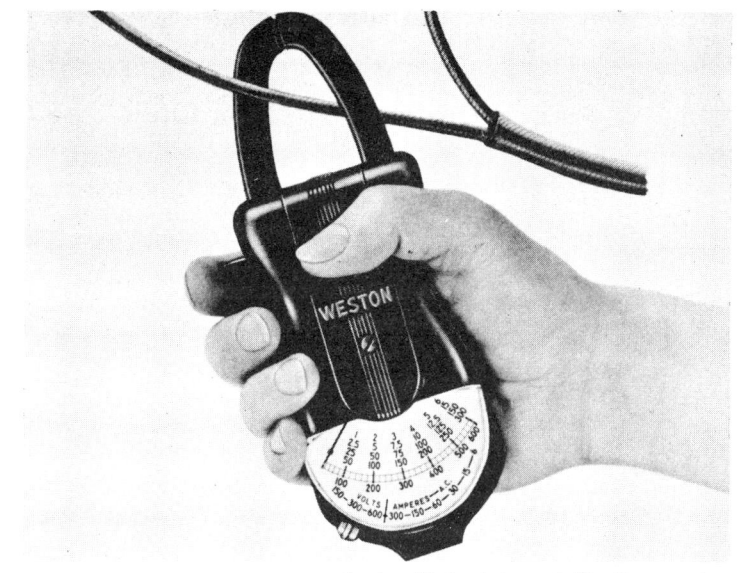

Courtesy Weston Instruments Div., Daystrom, Inc.
Fig. 1-5. Hook-on ammeter.

All four of the foregoing instruments may be combined into one convenient piece of test equipment, called an *analyzer* (Fig. 1-6).

ELECTRICAL TESTING

If you have more than normal aptitude or if you wish to tackle the more complicated repair jobs or major replacements, you will have to know more about the way a technician uses analyzing test instruments. The following discussion gives the highlights of the procedures followed by a technician when testing the various components found in appliances.

Line Voltage

Plug the leads from the appliance into the voltmeter, and the voltmeter leads into the outlet regularly used for the appliance. Turn the appliance on as well as any others connected to the same branch line.

Switches

Check with an ohmmeter for continuity across the terminals at each switch setting. **CAUTION: Before making any tests with an ohmmeter, remove the power plug from the outlet to prevent damaging the instrument.**

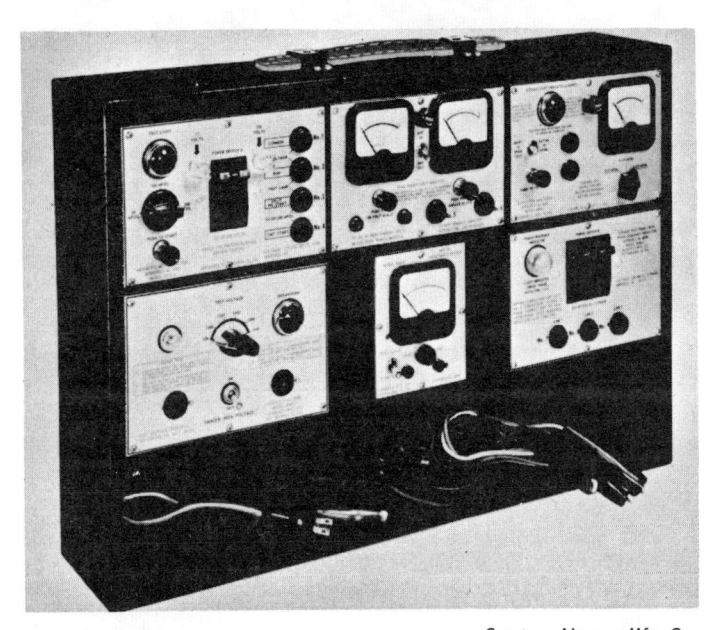

Courtesy Airserco Mfg. Co.

Fig. 1-6. An analyzer.

Overload Protectors

Use a wattmeter and a jumper wire to check the overload protector on compressors (Fig. 1-7). The jumper should be connected between terminals 1 and 2 on three-terminal overloads (*A* and *B* on some compressors). If higher than the specified wattage is consumed, the overload protector is probably good *if it opens the circuit*, and some other component of the system should be suspected. If wattage consumption is normal and removal of the

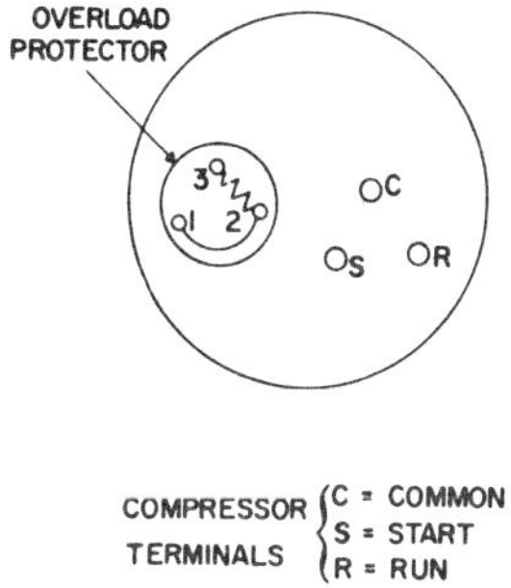

Fig. 1-7. Terminal arrangement of a typical overload protector.

COMPRESSOR TERMINALS { C = COMMON
S = START
R = RUN

jumper wire stops the compressor, the protector is defective and should be replaced.

Thermostats

Check for continuity with an ohmmeter connected across the terminals. Remove the lead wires, turn the thermostat to its high-limit setting, and connect the ohmmeter. No reading indicates a faulty thermostat—or possibly only dirty contacts.

Start Capacitors

If the motor draws excessive current or hums while starting (or does not start at all), the start capacitor may be faulty. A visual check will frequently disclose a white residue at or near the terminals, indicating a faulty capacitor. In the absence of any visual signs, the best test is to momentarily replace the old start capacitor with one of exactly the same specifications.

A capacitor can also be checked by making a resistance test; however, it must first be discharged. To do so, pull the power plug from the wall outlet and momentarily short across the capacitor terminals with a jumper wire. Set the ohmmeter on the 1-megohm scale. Take a reading across the capacitor terminals. Reverse the leads and take another reading; if the ohmmeter needle stabilizes at 30,000 ohms or less, the capacitor should be considered leaky and should be replaced.

Run Capacitor

Unexplainable excessive power consumption indicates a faulty run capacitor. Make the ohmmeter test described for the start capacitor. If the needle comes almost instantly to zero and slowly returns to infinity, the capacitor is functioning properly. If the needle does not move at all, the capacitor is open. If the needle comes to rest somewhere between zero and infinity, the capacitor is leaky. In either of the latter cases, the capacitor unit should be replaced.

Relays

Excessive wattage consumption of compressors in refrigerators, freezers, and air conditioners after reaching normal run speed could indicate a relay that is not properly dropping out of the circuit after start. Low line voltage will sometimes cause the relay to "chatter." To check, short out the relay with a jumper wire across the proper terminals. (Refer to the wiring diagram on manufacturers' service literature for the correct terminals to jump.) Apply the jumper wire while the compressor is running, but for no longer than 2 or 3 seconds at a time. If the compressor runs properly during the test, a faulty relay is indicated.

Circuit Lines

Use the continuity test light to check suspected lines in the circuit. For example, if a fan motor does not run, disconnect its leads and connect them to the probes of the test light. Always be sure that the appliance cycle is at the point where the inoperative component should be operating. This is usually accomplished by turning the timer dial to the proper setting.

Solenoids

Check across the terminals with an ohmmeter in the same manner as for a thermostat check. Here again, dirty contacts can cause trouble.

Timers

Check across each set of contact points with an ohmmeter, the same as for switches. Timers also get dirty contacts and fail to make contact.

PREVENTIVE MAINTENANCE

While it is not generally publicized, even in the owner's instruction manual, most appliances will require a minimum of preventive maintenance. This is particularly true of washers and dryers, whose parts generally operate faster and under greater load than other appliances. Any belt-driven appliance should be a candidate for preventive maintenance.

Sealed compressors and some washer transmissions, of course, never require lubrication, the lubricant being sealed inside the mechanical housing. However, all pulley wheels, drive wheels, cam surfaces, and other exposed mechanical parts should have regular attention, at least once a year. Large, exposed surfaces which bear on others (such as cam shafts) should be lightly coated with graphite or other suitable lubricant. Motor bearings need a drop or two of a good grade of motor oil three or four times a year. Water pumps are usually equipped with an oil wick for lubrication. This wick should be removed and soaked in turbine oil at least twice a year.

Some appliances boast "sealed" bearings on drive pulleys. Take this with a grain of salt—and a drop of oil. The best of these seals dry out after a year or two of use, permitting the lubricant to seep out. The sealed oil cup of these bearings should be pierced with an ice pick and lubricant applied regularly thereafter.

The need for lubrication is betrayed by squeaks and binding in the mechanical system. The presence of oil in drip pans, on the floor, or in other places where it should not be also indicates an investigation is necessary. Oil around a sealed compressor almost always indicates a serious failure has occurred, or is imminent, and should be traced to its source before further operation.

Tools

Any special tools required to accomplish servicing an appliance will be covered in the chapter dealing with the particular appliance. A set of good electrical tools and a set of mechanic's tools will, in most cases, be sufficient to accomplish the job. In addition, a wheel puller may be useful.

ELECTRIC MOTORS USED IN HOME APPLIANCES

The most common electric motors used in major appliances as the primary source of power are:

1. Split-phase induction motor.
2. Capacitor-start induction motor.
3. Permanent split-capacitor (PSC) motor.

An induction motor may be described as a motor having: a stationary field, called the stator, through which an electric current flows; and a rotor, fitted within the stator, but not touching it at any point. No electrical connections are made to the rotor. A magnetic field set up by current flowing through the stator coils is induced in the rotor, causing it to revolve at a constant speed.

Motors used in appliances for secondary functions, such as in pumps and fans, may be of the shaded-pole type. This is a low-output, low-speed motor with a relatively low starting power or torque. It has the advantage of design simplicity, well suited to a simple On-Off function. A shaded-pole motor ranges in horsepower from 1/300th to 1/30th hp.

Other desirable characteristics of motors for some applications are: (1) two-speed operation and (2) reversibility. Washers having "gentle" and "normal" speeds employ two-speed motors.

Split-Phase Motors

Single-phase electricity of the type commonly found in homes cannot by itself cause a motor to start rotating, because the magnetic field set up by single-phase current is stationary, and once aligned with this field, the rotor locks in the static position. Once the rotor can be induced to turn, however, its momentum is fed by the pulsing cycles of the current. The problem, then, is to provide a momentary boost to the motor so the rotor will begin to turn.

A split-phase motor (Fig. 1-8) has two windings: a start winding and a run winding. The start winding is composed of many turns of thin wire, setting up a high resistance. The run winding is composed of fewer turns of a heavy wire. The result is a "phase difference."

Fig. 1-8. Split-phase motor wiring diagram.

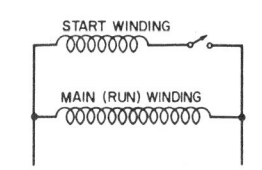

This phase difference between the start and run windings, both in the circuit momentarily, sets up magnetic forces of unequal strength and direction at different points around the circumference of the stator, causing the rotor to turn, no matter in what position it may have come to rest, in an effort to align itself with the unequal magnetic force. The slight movement then brings the rotor under the influence of a new magnetic direction, causing still more movement. The rapidly changing direction and strength of the rotating magnetic field cause the rotor to pick up speed and momentum.

Once the rotor has achieved run speed, a mechanical or electrical relay opens the circuit to the start winding and the run winding alone is energized. The run winding is sufficiently powerful to keep the motor operating at run speed.

Capacitor-Start, Induction-Run Motors

In a capacitor-start, induction-run motor (Fig. 1-9) the phase difference of two windings is still used at the start.

However, the starting torque is increased by means of an electrolytic start capacitor.

Capacitor-Start, Capacitor-Run Motors

In this type of motor (Fig. 1-10) an additional capacitor, called the run capacitor, is permitted to remain in the circuit even after the motor has started. The run capacitor increases the power of the motor.

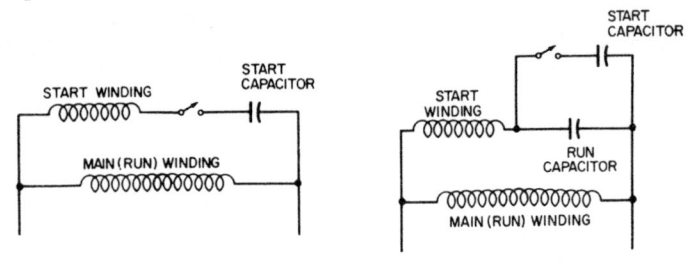

Fig. 1-9. Capacitor-start induction-run motor wiring diagram.

Fig. 1-10. Capacitor-start capacitor-run motor wiring diagram.

Permanent Split-Capacitor (PSC) Motor

The PSC motor (Fig. 1-11) has no start capacitors and relays, making it desirable from the point of view of economy; however, it has low starting torque (power), which limits its application. Briefly, the difference between a PSC motor and an ordinary split-phase motor is that the phase difference is permanent in the former; the run capacitor and auxiliary winding are never disconnected.

Because of its low starting torque, it can only be used in applications where the initial load is not great. This means that it may be used to power compressors whose

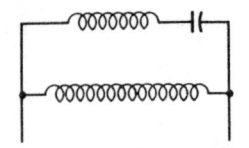

Fig. 1-11. Permanent split-capacitor PSC motor wiring diagram.

head pressure is relieved during cycle-off periods, such as in air conditioners. This is the reason behind the delay requested of the operator of some air conditioners between stopping and starting. Starting the compressor immediately after a stop forces the motor to attempt to start under a full load, which it was never designed to do—damage may result.

Two-Speed Motors

Speed selection in induction-type motors is achieved through the use of two run windings, in addition to the start winding. An electrical switch sends current through only one of these windings for high speed, or connects both of them in parallel for low speed.

Reversible Motors

By crossing the leads to an electric motor, polarity is reversed and the rotor turns in the opposite direction. Crossing the wires is accomplished by a switch, which is sometimes operated by a solenoid energized by the timer.

PERFORMANCE CHECKS

There is not much that can happen to an electric motor itself; most motor failures are caused by defective auxiliary components, such as relays and capacitors, rather than by defects in the rotor or stator. Replacement of the defective component is normally a simple task, since most such components are mounted outside the motor housing.

If a burnout occurs, of course, the entire stator and rotor must be either replaced or rewound. There are shops that specialize in rewinding rotors and, more recently, shops that also take on the more difficult task of rewinding stators. In normal practice, an exchange is made on a one-for-one basis, plus the cost of rebuilding.

In checking the performance of a motor, first make sure that the line voltage and frequency are the same as those listed on the motor or appliance nameplate. If the motor is of the type that can operate on either 120 or 240 volts, make sure the leads are connected properly as indicated at the appliance terminal box.

Run the motor momentarily without load to check start and direction of rotation. Leads are sometimes crossed in reassembly, which causes the motor to change direction. Check by the sound of the motor whether or not the start winding is properly dropping out of the circuit within 2 or 3 seconds after start.

Check branch line fuses to be certain that the amperage rating of the fuse is at least 20% higher than the amperage rating of the motor.

Inspect all bearing surfaces on the motor for signs of lack of lubrication. By the same token, try turning belts, gear trains, and other mechanisms by hand to uncover any signs of mechanical binding.

Check wiring connections to insure that wiring is according to the wiring diagram sometimes provided on the appliance itself. Check for adequate grounding, particularly with rubber-mounted motors. Look for a grounding wire sometimes hidden in one of the rubber feet on the base. Make a clean connection by scraping off any dirt or grease at the terminal connections. Check base and mounting for loose or insecure fastenings. Check and reset buttons with which the motor overload may be equipped.

If a failure has occurred and the motor is suspected, disconnect the wiring harness from the motor and test across the terminals, using your series test lamp. Be sure that the motor overload is not in the open position. If the test lamp glows, the trouble is not in the motor. If an open test results, check each component, such as relays, capacitors, etc., in turn, making the tests described earlier in this chapter. Remember, when replacing start capacitors, to replace the relay as well.

CHAPTER 2

REFRIGERATORS AND FREEZERS

A refrigeration system can be summed up in a few words. It is a mechanical system of tubes of varying inside diameter through which is pumped a refrigerant under alternating high and low pressure. In the "high side" of the system (Fig. 2-1), the refrigerant is under compression, causing it to give up its heat and condense to a liquid. The greater part of the high side is separate from the refrigerated space so that heat is discharged outside the cabinet. In the "low side" of the system (inside the refrigerator cabinet), the liquid refrigerant expands to a vapor, thus absorbing heat. Repeated circulation of the refrigerant will gradually cool down the refrigerated space to the desired temperature.

Now, each of the components of a refrigeration system will be examined in detail. (Start at the compressor in Fig. 2-1 and read the diagram counterclockwise.)

HOW A REFRIGERATOR WORKS

The *compressor* receives hot refrigerant vapor from the *suction line* in the low side, compresses it, and sends it through the *discharge line* into the *condenser*. The condenser is located outside the refrigerated space, usually at the back of the cabinet. When the refrigerated vapor enters the condenser it contains heat.

The condenser on most refrigerators and freezers is so designed and located that a natural draft of room air is generated around and through the fins which surround the condenser tubing.

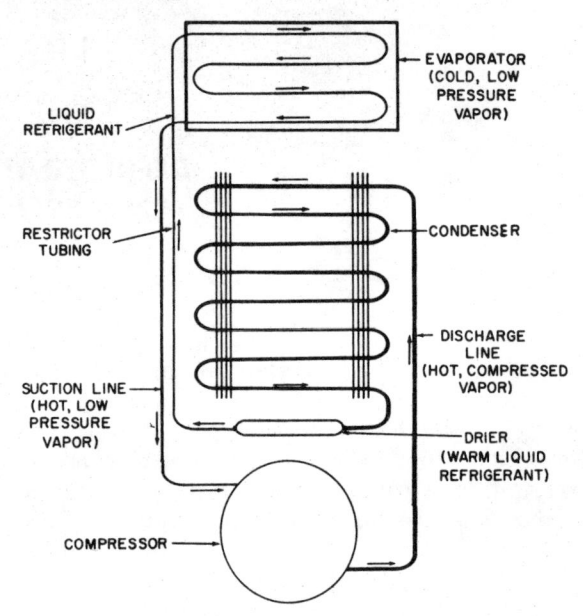

Fig. 2-1. Refrigerator schematic diagram.

The heat contained in the vapor (obeying the law that heat passes from substances of higher temperature to substances of lower temperature) passes into the fins of the condenser, from which it passes to the cooler air flowing past the fins. When the refrigerant vapor reaches the last passes (a pass is a turn of the copper tubing) of the condenser, it has become cool enough to condense to a liquid.

From the condenser, the liquid refrigerant passes into the *liquid line* and back into the refrigerator cabinet. Here, it enters the *restrictor*, a length of copper tubing which acts like a dam to separate the high side of the system from the low side. Having an inside diameter of only a few hundredths of an inch, the restrictor allows only a small flow of liquid refrigerant to enter the evaporator.

In the *evaporator*, which has tubing of much larger diameter, the liquid refrigerant is suddenly able to expand. In order to do so, it must "borrow" energy from its surroundings to motivate the molecules to travel the greater distances involved. The energy it needs is present in the form of heat in the air immediately surrounding the evaporator. The refrigerant traveling through the evaporator absorbs the heat surrounding it (Fig. 2-2).

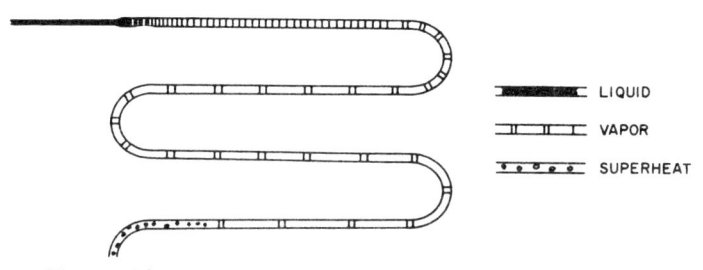

Fig. 2-2. Three stages of the refrigerant in the cooling tubes.

The temperature of the refrigerant liquid and vapor has not been raised by even 1 degree until the point is reached in the vaporization process where all the liquid refrigerant boils away. However, toward the end of its travel in the evaporator, where complete vaporization has taken place, the refrigerant vapor now begins to grow warmer since it no longer needs the energy. It is now called *superheated vapor*, or *superheat*. The hot refrigerant vapor now passes into the suction line, and once again into the compressor, where the cycle starts over again.

A certain amount of superheat is provided for in a refrigeration system. This is to prevent the possibility of any unvaporized (liquid) refrigerant from entering the compressor. Since liquids are largely incompressible, liquid in the compressor would cause loud knocking noises and possible damage to the delicate leaf valves inside.

The evaporator is located near the top of the cabinet interior in all refrigerators and freezers. As the air surrounding the evaporator gives up its heat, it tends to sink to the bottom of the cabinet (cold air sinks, warm air rises). This stirs up the air at the bottom, displacing it so that it rises to the top (Fig. 2-3). Thus, a continuous circulation of the air is always taking place within the cabinet.

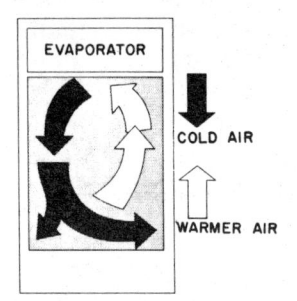

Fig. 2-3. Air circulation within the refrigerator cabinet.

Since heat flows from substances of higher temperature to substances of lower temperature, any object at room temperature which is placed within the refrigerator will soon give up its own heat to the cooler air in the cabinet. This air in turn releases its heat to the energy-starved refrigerant liquid in the evaporator. The continuous cycling of the refrigerant through the evaporator gradually cools the interior of the refrigerator or freezer (and all its contents) to the desired temperature.

The Compressor

The heart of a refrigeration system is the motor compressor. Most, if not all, refrigeration systems are of the "closed" type, which is to say that the compressor pump and the electric motor that powers it are all contained in a sealed shell through which the refrigerant also travels.

The compressor is simply a pump designed to handle vapor through a system of leaf valves. Power for the pump is obtained through an electric motor mounted within the same shell, which is sealed to prevent the entrance of dirt, outside air, and moisture. A suction-line inlet through which refrigerant vapor is admitted is located somewhere near the top of the compressor housing. In most compressors, the hot vapor is free to travel throughout the interior of the compressor and motor housing.

In order to prevent damage to the compressor due to an overload or some other condition which would put a heavy drain on the current supplied to the motor, an overload protector is introduced into the circuit just before it reaches the motor windings.

Controls

It is obvious that if the refrigerant were allowed to cycle without interruption, it would eventually bring the temperature of the interior down to its own temperature, which might be as low as minus 40°F. at 0.6 pound per square inch. This would be far too cold for proper storage of refrigerated foods.

The principal means of controlling the temperature of the interior is by cycling the motor compressor on and off. As long as the motor compressor is not operating, the refrigerant is permitted to remain at a uniform pressure throughout the system, and no refrigeration takes place.

A *thermostat* (Fig. 2-4), accomplishes the compressor cycling by its unique ability to sense changes in temperature. This device is nothing more than a hollow tube with a bulb at one end and an expanding and contracting bellows at the other. This assembly is filled with a small amount of the refrigerant used in the main refrigerating system. The sensing bulb is placed in the evaporator so that it responds to temperature changes occurring at the source of the cold air. With the compressor running, the evaporator becomes colder, and the refrigerant in the sensing bulb contracts, reducing the pressure at the bellows end. A spring overcomes the expansion of the bellows, and it begins to collapse. At a predetermined point in the travel of the bellows another spring mechanism causes an electric switch to snap open, interrupting the flow of current to the compressor (Fig. 2-5).

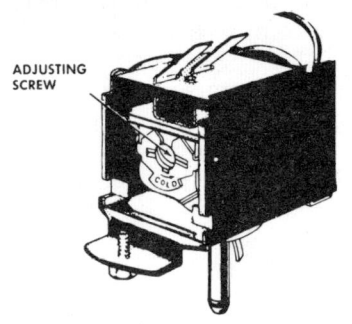

Fig. 2-4. Thermostat control assembly.

Fig. 2-5. Compressor control switch.

With the compressor stopped, a gradual warmup occurs in the evaporator as heat from the room penetrates the cabinet. This causes the refrigerant vapor in the sensing bulb to expand, pushing the bellows against the force of the spring. At the upper end of the range of temperatures prescribed for the thermostat, the spring mechanism of the electric switch forces the contacts to snap closed, and electricity flows to the compressor, causing it to start.

Electrical switches in any household appliance are manufactured to open and close with a positive action. If the contacts were permitted to approach each other slowly, they would reach a point where the electricity would jump the short distance between them, accompanied by a hot spark. This condition, called *arcing*, would soon burn out the contacts if allowed to occur often enough. The snap provided by the spring mechanism minimizes this condition.

Thermostats may be set through two main adjustments—the *range* and *differential*. The range of a thermostat is set by the manufacturer and should only be adjusted by qualified servicemen. Adjustment is usually accomplished by means of a screw located beneath the differential knob.

Range determines the cut-in and cut-out temperatures at which the compressor will cycle on and off. Extreme changes in the adjustment may cause the refrigerator to cycle on and off through a range of temperatures wholly inadequate for proper food storage.

The differential adjustment is intended for use by the owner and is accomplished by turning a numbered dial. The numbers usually have no relationship to any actual temperature, but are merely used for reference. The differential setting will raise or lower the cut-out temperature only; it does not affect the cut-in temperature, which is usually fixed at from 34°F to 39°F. This ensures that interior temperatures in the refrigerator will not fall below the point necessary for proper food storage, and on automatic defrost models, that defrosting will take place on schedule.

The effect of a low-temperature setting of the differential knob is to cause the compressor to run for a longer period of time before cut-out, and for shorter periods at the higher temperature settings.

DEFROSTING

When warm air passes over a cool object, the air in contact with the object gives up its moisture in the form of droplets of water. The more humid the air and the greater the contrast of temperature between the air and the object, the more rapid is the formation of the condensate.

A refrigerator evaporator, the ice trays, cooling plate, and other components nearby are in a very cold state. When the refrigerator door is opened, a mass of warm air is admitted into the interior of the cabinet. This air passing over the cold components releases its moisture in the form of water. The water then freezes on the cold component, eventually building up a thick coating of frost.

The more often the refrigerator door is opened and the more humid and warm the air which is admitted to the interior, the more rapidly will frost form on the evaporator.

Frost hampers the free exchange of heat between the air in the cabinet interior, evaporator fins, and coils so that it must be removed periodically; the removal process is called defrosting.

In many models, defrosting is accomplished semiautomatically. The defrost switch is turned to the Defrost position, which shuts off the current to the compressor. Warm water placed in a pan under the evaporator may be used to melt the frost, or the user may let defrosting proceed with no further attention. When the evaporator has reached a predetermined high and all ice has melted off the surfaces, the circuit to the compressor is closed automatically by means of a temperature-sensing thermostat, and the refrigerator resumes normal operation of its own accord.

Fully automatic defrosting, which is called by a variety of names, is intended more to prevent frost from forming than to remove it once it has formed. The *initiation* of the defrost cycle is accomplished in one of two ways. In the first method, a cam on the bottom of the refrigerator door trips a counter mechanism. When the door has been opened and closed a predetermined number of times, the counter closes a defrost-cycle circuit and defrosting begins.

In the second method, an automatic timer is energized each time the compressor operates. The timer functions only during the period of compressor operation. After about 12 hours of accumulated running time, a spring mechanism operates and the defrost cycle circuit is closed.

A less frequently used method of initiating the defrost cycle depends on the actual physical build-up of frost. A spring-loaded button is gradually pushed toward a contact by the increasing thickness of ice forming on the evaporator. When the ice has reached a predetermined thickness, the button trips a spring mechanism, which in turn causes the defrost-cycle circuit to close. Since this method depends on the thickness of the ice, it cannot in truth be called a "no-frost" or "frost-free" system.

The actual process of defrosting can also be accomplished in several ways. In the first of two of the more popular ways, a heating coil is employed directly beneath the evaporator. As the defrost cycle is initiated, the compressor circuit is opened and the heat-coil circuit closed. The heater, giving off intense heat for a short period, quickly melts the ice without affecting the interior temperature of the cabinet too drastically.

As the ice melts, the resultant water drips into a drain pan, through drain channels in the wall of the refrigerator, and into a condensate pan beneath the condenser. Here, it is permitted to evaporate into room air, the process being sometimes hastened by either a condenser fan, heater coil, or both.

When the temperature of the refrigerator cabinet reaches a predetermined high (approximately 45°F.), a defrost terminating thermostat closes the circuit to the compressor and opens the circuit to the heater coil. The refrigerator now resumes normal operation.

The other method of defrosting, and one that seems to be in more widespread use, causes the refrigerant to bypass the condenser temporarily so that the evaporator, instead of cooling the space, now functions exactly the same as the condenser (Fig. 2-7). Here's how it works:

The defrost initiator mechanism energizes a defrost solenoid valve. This valve (Fig. 2-6) offers the refrigerant flow a choice of two channels. In the closed position (normal refrigeration), the refrigerant travels through the condenser and into the valve through Inlet A, emerging at C and into the evaporator. In this position, the refrigerant has been acted on by the condenser, so that it is in a cooled state when it emerges at C.

In the open position (defrost cycle operating), the refrigerant may enter the valve at both Inlet A and Inlet B. Inlet B is the channel for the refrigerant that has bypassed the condenser (Fig. 2-7); thus it is the path of

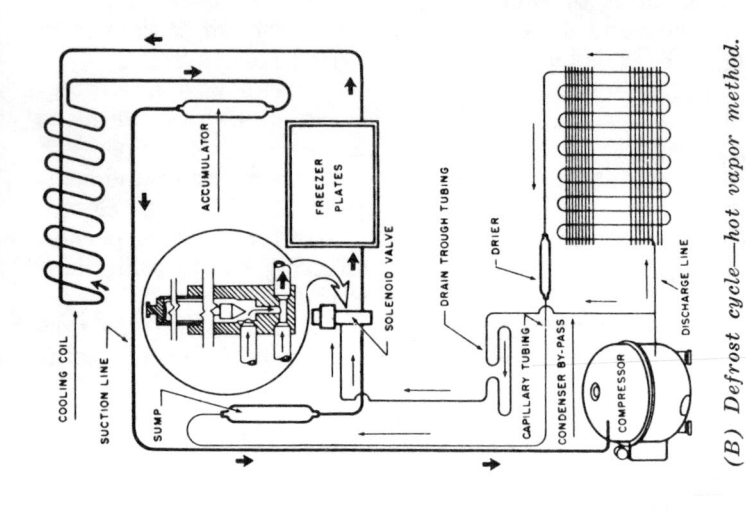

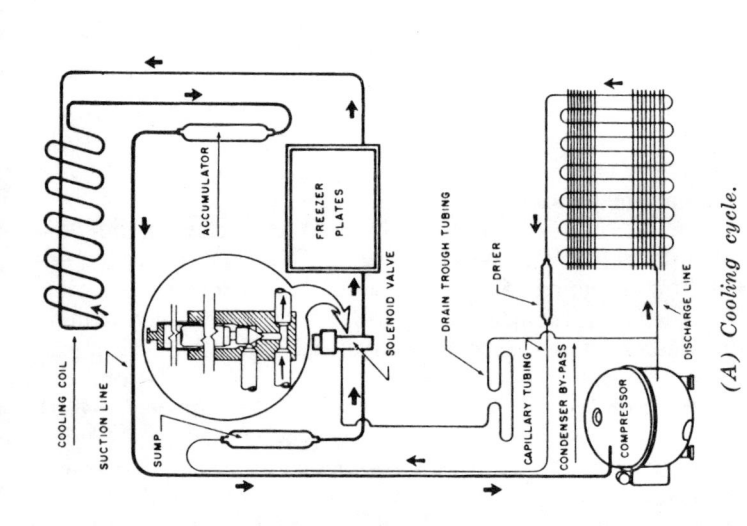

Fig. 2-6. Refrigerator schematic.

(A) Cooling cycle.

(B) Defrost cycle—hot vapor method.

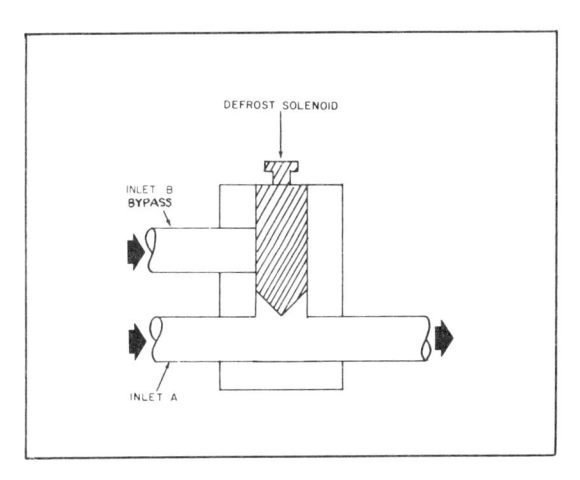

Fig. 2-7. Defrost solenoid valve in closed position.

least resistance. The flow to the condenser, however, is not entirely restricted, because dangerous pressures would be built up in the condenser if this were the case. The diagram shows that refrigerant may still be admitted into the valve at Inlet A, indicating that the condenser flow is still open, along with the bypass flow.

The net effect of the valve is to admit hot refrigerant vapor to the evaporator for a short period of time. Since vapor normally leaves the compressor at approximately 120°F., the thin film of ice which may have formed on the evaporator since the last defrost cycle quickly melts away.

As in the heater-coil defrost cycle, a defrost terminating thermostat breaks the circuit to the solenoid valve when a predetermined high has been reached, and the refrigerant vapor proceeds on its normal course through the condenser and restrictor tubing.

REFRIGERATOR/FREEZER COMBINATIONS

Many popular models contain two separate compartments, each heavily insulated from the other. Each compartment operates at a different temperature, the refrigerator section being maintained at a user-selected temperature which may range from 34°F. to 42°F., while the temperature in the freezer section is normally kept at approximately 0°F. This temperature difference is achieved in several ways in existing refrigerator/freezers.

While it may appear that a refrigerator/freezer combination has two separate evaporators, it is actually only one unit, with some of its passes in the freezer section and some in the refrigerator section (Fig. 2-8). In earlier model refrigerators, the difference in temperature in the two compartments was achieved through the use of a solenoid valve and a bypass refrigerant-flow circuit (Fig.

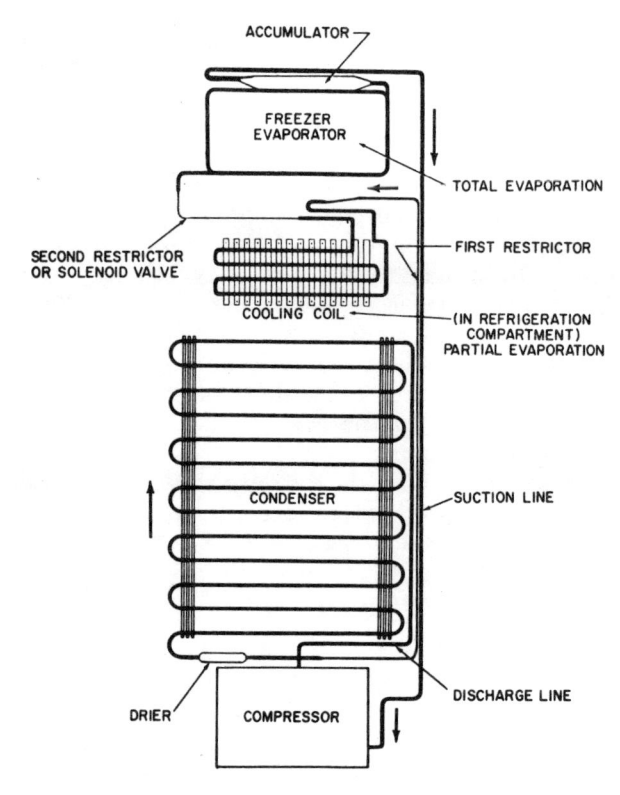

Fig. 2-8. Two-compartment cooling.

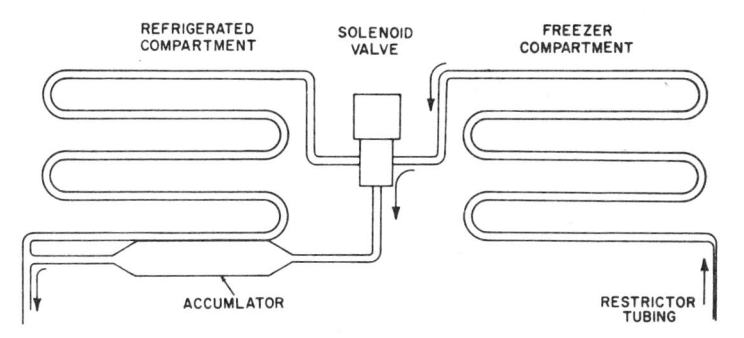

Fig. 2-9. Early method of temperature-difference control.

2-9). When the refrigerator compartment temperature reached a predetermined low, the solenoid valve was energized by an electrical circuit closed through a sensing thermostat in the refrigeration section. The valve diverted the flow of refrigerant, bypassing the refrigerator compartment passes of the evaporator so that the refrigerant traveled only through the freezer section passes.

In another method, a differential pressure-control (DPC) valve is employed (Fig. 2-10). The DPC valve is located in the evaporator passes between the refrigerator

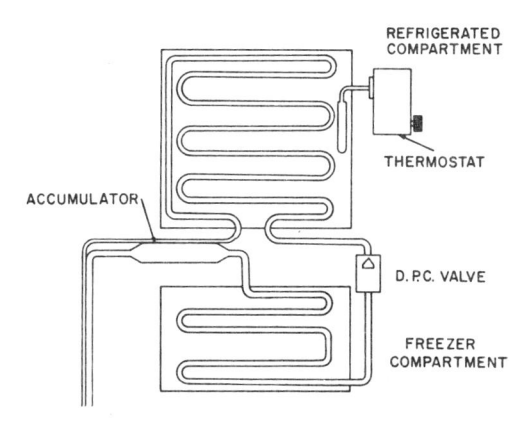

Fig. 2-10. Differential pressure-control valve method of two-compartment cooling.

37

and the freezer compartments. Just ahead of the refrigerator evaporator, the usual restrictor tubing causes a moderate pressure drop in the refrigerator section of the evaporator, permitting only a portion of the refrigerant to boil, but maintaining most of the refrigerant in a liquid state until it reaches the DPC valve. At this point, just ahead of the freezer evaporator, the pressure drop becomes much greater, causing the refrigerant boiling point to drop to an equivalent temperature of minus 5°F. (obeying the positive relationship between the pressure of a vapor and its temperature). Control of the DPC valve is achieved by hand settings on a dial, which varies the amount of flow obstruction, increasing or decreasing the drop in pressure to achieve a variety of temperatures.

A third method of achieving a difference in temperature between the freezer and refrigerator sections is by varying the evaporator surface area in the two compartments (Fig. 2-11). In this method, a balance is achieved by the engineer in the design of the system, taking into account the volume of the spaces to be refrigerated. A plate is mounted on the wall of the refrigerator compartment; this plate usually consists of two pieces of metal pressed together in such a way that channels are left open between the two through which the refrigerant may travel. The size of the plate in relation to the cubic volume to be refrigerated is carefully calculated so that even though the temperature at any one point on the surface of the plate reaches 0°F., the average temperature of the refrigerated space remains at a constant 38°F. to 42°F., and the freezer stays at 0°F.

Miscellaneous Components

Dryer—Water will affect the efficiency of a refrigeration system because it will not vaporize at the pressures and temperatures associated with refrigerants, but will pass through in a liquid or even a frozen state. Since liquids are incompressible, any water in the system will overload the motor compressor and may even damage the valves and other controls, as was mentioned previously.

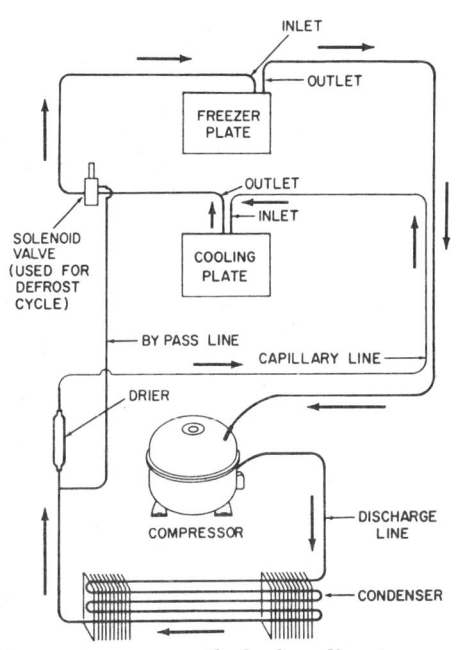

Fig. 2-11. Evaporator-area method of cooling two compartments.

Only 10 or 12 parts of water *per million parts of refrigerant* can be tolerated in a refrigeration system.

Dryers are introduced into the refrigerant line between the condenser and the capillary to extract any water or other impurities that may be present. The dryer contains activated alumina, silica gel, calcium sulphate, or other dehydrating agents with an affinity for water. As the refrigerant flows through the dryer, the water and other impurities it may contain are trapped and held.

Heat Exchanger—Usually not a component as such in a household refrigerator, the heat exchanger is simply the meeting of the suction and discharge lines, taped or soldered together in intimate contact for part of their travel. The (relatively) warm refrigerant liquid passing through the capillary on its way to the evaporator gives up some of its heat to the cooler refrigerant vapor in the suction line. This does two things—(1) it increases the pressure of the vapor in the suction line, thereby improving the efficiency of the compressor; and (2) it acts as extra insurance that the liquid refrigerant will not vaporize prematurely before it enters the capillary and the evaporator.

Accumulator—This component serves as a vessel for any unevaporated liquid emerging from the evaporator. It is particularly useful in split evaporators where only part of the evaporator is in use, as in a convertible refrigerator/freezer.

The outlet from the accumulator, also called a *header*, is located above the surface of any liquid it may contain, passing only vapor into the suction line.

Freezers

Freezers, of course, work on exactly the same principle as refrigerators, with the exception that the temperatures employed are about 40°F. lower than those in a typical refrigerator. Some freezers provide two settings, Sharp Freeze, and Frozen Food Storage. The Sharp Freeze position of the operating dial simply cycles the compressor to run continuously until the customer returns the dial to Frozen Food Storage, the normal setting. Temperatures inside the cabinet during Sharp Freeze will fall to minus 20°F. or below, depending on how long the compressor is permitted to operate. Normal operation of a freezer maintains an inside temperature of approximately 0°F., and is accomplished by the cycling on and off of the compressor, as regulated by a thermostat.

Evaporator—The evaporator in a freezer usually takes the form of a series of "wrapper" coils which are imbedded in the space between the liner and the outer shell (Fig. 2-12). This arrangement insures the even distribution of zero cold throughout the roomy cabinet interior.

ELECTRICAL SYSTEM

Most household refrigerators run on 120-volt, 60-cycle, single-phase ac, such as commonly supplied to homes in

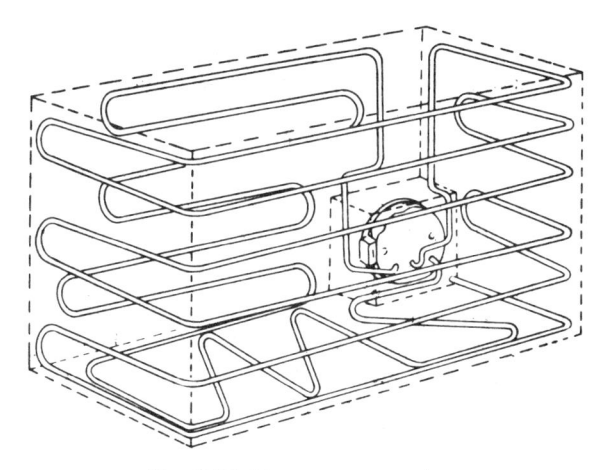

Fig. 2-12. Freezer evaporator.

the United States. A simplified wiring diagram for a single-temperature, single-door refrigerator is shown in Fig. 2-13. Note how the compressor circuit may be completely disconnected from the main refrigerator circuit by a service-cord plug.

Current flows through the door-light switch to the interior electric lamp and to one set of contacts at the thermostat. The second wire of the power cord feeds current directly to the same contact on the thermostat. When the contact is closed, current is permitted to flow to the motor compressor through the motor-compressor service cord.

Current now flows to the overload protector and, under normal conditions, is uninterrupted. Should a current-drain or high-voltage condition occur, the contacts would be broken and the circuit opened. When the overload condition subsides, the protector returns to its normal position, and the current is again permitted to flow.

PERFORMANCE CHECKS

There are two ways to check the performance of a refrigerator or freezer (or any other major appliance run by electricity). The first is a mechanical check, the second is an electrical test; both methods can be used in diagnosing the source of trouble in a refrigeration system.

Mechanical Checks

Visual—Check all components for visible signs of damage or wear (such as kinks, nicks, or breaks in re-

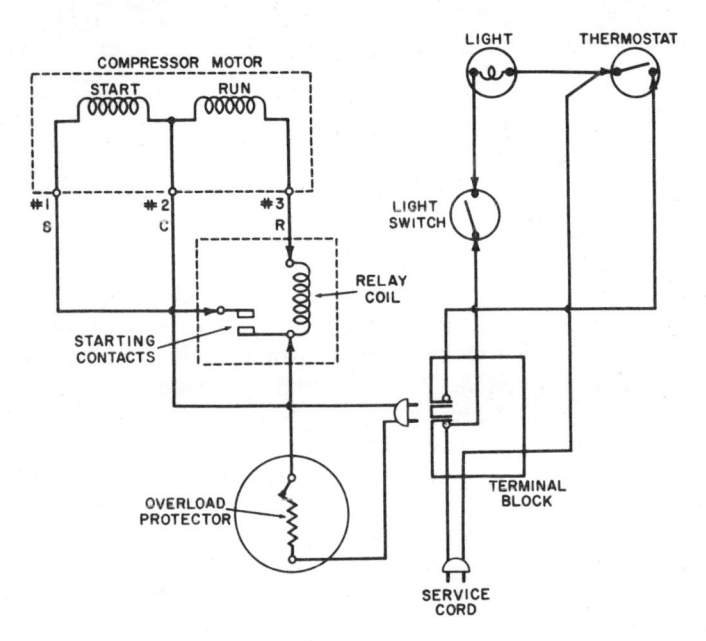

Fig. 2-13. Simple refrigerator wiring diagram.

frigerant tubing), excessive frost on cold components, unevaporated water in drain pans, signs of compressor burnout, the presence of oil in or near the compressor, and other abnormal conditions. One of the most common causes of inefficient operation is dirt or dust clogging the condenser tubing and fins.

You can also learn something from the *feel* of discharge and suction lines. The discharge line should feel hot to the touch, but not too hot to handle. The suction line should feel tepid. Cold spots along liquid lines usually mean an obstruction in the line, which is also betrayed by sweating *ahead* of any possible obstruction.

Temperature Check—The interior of the cabinet may be checked for proper temperature by using a thermometer with a range above 32°F. Select a container of liquid or a mass of food such as a loaf of bread which has been stored in the refrigerator for at least 12 hours prior to the check. Immerse, or bury, the tip of the thermometer so that it reaches the center of the liquid or food and close the refrigerator door. Wait a few minutes for the thermometer to stabilize, then read the temperature while the tip is still immersed. Do not make the temperature check with food that has been stored in or near the evaporator, but instead select that which is near the center of the refrigerated space.

Running-Time Check—There are so many variables involved in the length of time that a compressor is cycled on that it is hardly worth the effort to make a running-time check. Room temperature, humidity, how recently a warm mass of food was put away, and the differential setting of the thermostat all have an effect on running time. In addition, some of the automatic defrost or frost-free refrigerators run so nearly continuously that you would have to sit idly by waiting for the compressor to cycle off. In most cases, manufacturers have discontinued giving running time averages in service literature. Excessive running time, therefore, is not of itself a sign of system failure.

Leak Test—Modern refrigerants are colorless and odorless, and are therefore almost impossible to detect by sight or smell. One of the surest signs of a refrigerant leak is the presence of oil at any point in the system. Oil mixes intimately with refrigerant liquid and vapor and is present throughout the interior of the tubing and components. Any refrigerant leak is therefore sure to be accompanied by some oil.

Unit Analysis—If any of the following conditions are

the only ones encountered in servicing the refrigerator or freezer, the compressor *need not* be replaced:

a. High-side leak resulting in partial or complete loss of refrigerant charge.
b. Low-side leaks in the components located *outside* the refrigerated space.
c. Too much refrigerant charge (a rare condition, unless the system has been opened since manufacture).
d. Too little refrigerant charge (only a technician with proper equipment can determine this for you).
e. The presence of moisture in the system as a result of low-side leaks in the components located *outside* the refrigerated space.
f. Moisture in the line due to high-side leaks.

Replacement of the compressor is *always* indicated under any of the following conditions:

a. Broken tubing (provided the unit has been operating with the broken tubing. If the unit has never been operated, however, no compressor replacement is necessary).
b. Any leak detected in the low side of the system in any component located *within* the refrigerated space.
c. Particles of burned-out motor windings detected in any part of the system.
d. Oil and refrigerant leaks at the compressor terminals, housing welds, or tubing joints at or near the compressor.
e. Noisy or stuck compressor, or a compressor that runs without pumping.

Electrical Tests

The following electrical tests are designed to tell whether or not a particular component is open, or shorted, and whether it requires repair or replacement. It also gives other information of value in diagnosing the cause of a failure.

Line Voltage—Line voltage should be read with the refrigerator running under normal load at the time of the test. Other appliances in the home which would normally operate at the same time should also be turned on.

Switch Terminals—Place a test lamp across the various contacts in the switch. If the lamp fails to light, a defective switch is indicated.

Relay Test—Excessive consumption of power by the compressor on reaching run speed could indicate a relay that is not dropping out of the circuit properly after start. Low line voltage will sometimes cause the relay to "chatter." To check this, short out the relay with a jumper wire across the proper terminals (refer to the manufacturer's literature to determine which terminals to jumper). Apply the short during compressor run for no more than 2 or 3 seconds at a time. If the compressor runs properly during the test, a faulty relay is indicated.

Capacitor Test—The easiest test for a defective capacitor is to replace it with one known to be good. Be sure to replace it with a capacitor of exactly the same microfarad rating.

Wiring Test—Check for broken wires by visual inspection as far as possible, or by placing a test cord between various components in turn until the break is isolated.

Solenoid Test (Two-Temperature Models and Convertibles)—With this unit operating in normal refrigeration cycle, place a test lamp across the terminals of the initiator mechanism (counter cam, defrost-cycle timer, or hand switch). If the lamp fails to glow, the solenoid coil is shorted (provided the wiring harness is unbroken).

COMMON REFRIGERATOR AND FREEZER REPAIRS

To keep failures to a minimum, remember the following points:

1. The number and lengths of time a refrigerator or freezer door is opened will greatly add to the accumulation of frost on the evaporator. A table placed

on the door-handle side and adjusted to the refrigerator will cut down on frost accumulation by reducing the number of trips to the refrigerator from the sink, etc., leaving the door open between trips.
2. Those models without automatic defrosting should be defrosted regularly—about twice as frequently in hot as in cold weather. Frost should never be permitted to build up to a thick coating on the evaporator, because this reduces heat transfer and impairs the efficiency of the unit. Frost also traps and holds food odors.
3. Clean the condenser (if of the exposed type) regularly with a long bristle brush on the end of a vacuum cleaner tube. Dirt on the condenser clogs the natural draft of air and drastically cuts refrigerating efficiency.

TROUBLESHOOTING GUIDE

The following "symptoms" are the signs of trouble in the system. Each symptom is followed by a number of possible causes and remedies. The list is by no means complete, but it will serve as a guide to the more common failures and causes of failure in a refrigerator or freezer system.

Unit Will Not Operate, No Interior Light

1. Power cord removed from or loose in wall outlet.
2. Blown fuse. Check line voltage at outlet. Voltage should be no more than 10% higher or lower than normal. Check for an excessive number of appliances working off the same branch line. Replace fuse.

Unit Will Not Operate, Interior Light On

1. Defective switches. Test switches as outlined previously.
2. Defective thermostat. Test as outlined previously.
3. Defective relay. Test as outlined previously.
4. Defective overload protector. Test as outlined previously.

5. Defective capacitor. Replace.
6. Open or shorted compressor. Test as outlined previously.
7. Broken lead wires. Visual inspection or test as outlined previously.

No Defrosting Cycle

1. Initiator mechanism defective. Test by visual inspection or with test lamp across wiring terminals. Manually rotate cam to test for free movement.
2. Open or shorted solenoid valve coil. With the solenoid control in the position which normally supplies current to the valve, test across wiring terminals.

Unit Runs Continuously, Cabinet Warm

1. Extreme hot weather conditions may contribute to symptom.
2. Poor door seal at gasket.
3. Interior light may stay on when door is closed. Check door light switch.

Unit Runs Continuously, Cabinet Cold

1. Defective thermostat.

Defrost Water Not Evaporating

1. If defrost vaporizer coil is employed, check across terminals with test lamp.
2. Condenser fan defective. Check fan motor with test lamp.

Noisy Operation

1. Check for misaligned fan blades, loose tubing connections (particularly around motor compressor), defective fan motor bearings, or loose compressor mountings.
2. If noise seems to come from within the compressor and does not stop after the unit has been in operation for a short time, internal trouble is indicated, such as broken internal mountings, loose shaft bear-

ings, or worn piston rings. Compressor should be given compression test or replaced.
3. If the noise is a loud click at start, it indicates that the motor overload protector is operating. This is not a bad sign in itself, but it is an indication that an overload condition is being encountered. If condition persists, make a unit analysis.
4. High head pressure may cause noisy operation of the compressor. Check for extremely clogged condition around condenser fins.

CHAPTER 3

WASHING MACHINES

Modern washers can be divided roughly into two main groups—the automatic type (further subdivided into tumbler and agitator), and the conventional type (subdivided into wringer and twin-tub washers).

TUMBLER WASHERS

Most tumbler washers are "front loading," meaning that the clothes are placed in the washer through a door that opens to the front. A few tumbler washers have borrowed a page out of the commercial laundry book and provided a door on the circumference of the cylinder basket through which the clothes are loaded or removed.

The cylindrical basket of a tumbler washer rotates in a horizontal plane—that is, its axis is parallel to the floor (Fig. 3-1). In some models the axis is inclined slightly, sloping to the rear. Agitation of the clothes occurs by lifting them out of the soapy water by means of the rotating basket, and letting them fall back into the water by their own weight as they reach the top of the revolution.

The cylinder basket revolves slowly (about 50 rpm) during the wash and rinse periods, at the end of which the water is drained from the machine. The cylinder basket then revolves much faster (600 rpm for "normal action," 300 rpm for "gentle action") to spin the clothes damp dry and ready for final drying.

Because there is no agitator in a tumbler washer, contruction tends to be somewhat simpler, requiring only a means to spin the cylinder basket at two (or three) different speeds.

AGITATOR WASHERS

Agitator washers are loaded from the top. In this type the axis of the cylinder basket is vertical to the floor (Fig. 3-2), and the basket does not spin during the wash or agitation cycle. Instead, an agitator oscillates in the

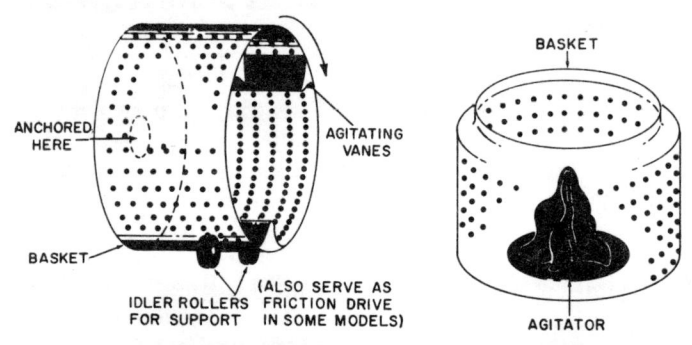

Fig. 3-1. Cylinder basket of a tumbler-type washer.

Fig. 3-2. Agitator-type washer cylinder basket.

tub, sloshing the water and the clothes through an arc of about 180°. Some agitators have a vertical motion as well, and still others incline the plane of movement from the vertical, causing an undulating motion. These additional motions are designed to create greater turbulence in the water for maximum loosening of dirt.

AUTOMATIC WASHERS

An automatic washing machine is probably the most complicated piece of machinery in the modern home (see block diagram, Fig. 3-3). It is complicated because it is required to perform a great many functions in the course of the complete washing cycle.

The act of turning on the machine actually does no more than close circuits to the drive and timer motors. The drive motor in most machines is coupled to (1) the

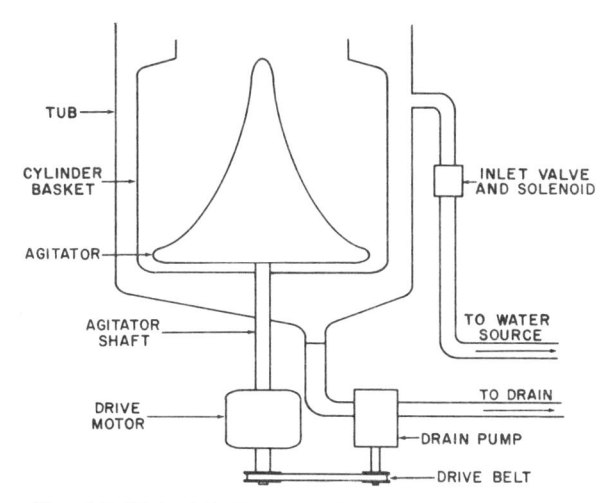

Fig. 3-3. Pictorial diagram of an automatic washer.

agitator or, in tumbler washers, the cylinder basket, and (2) a water pump. A secondary circuit in the electrical system feeds current to a timer motor which controls all the operations of the machine during the entire wash and spin cycles.

When the user turns the various selector dials for the type of washing desired (Fig. 3-4), a set of cams is aligned, presetting a switch and adjusting a pair of water-

Fig. 3-4. Automatic-washer control panel.

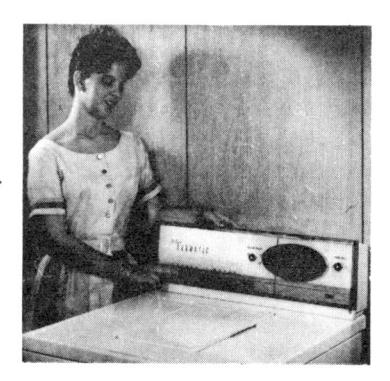

inlet valves. If the machine offers a choice of either normal or gentle action, a different set of cam wheels is brought into play for the selection made. These cam wheels are revolved slowly by the timer motor. As they revolve, their surfaces make contact with switches at various points in their travel, opening and closing circuits to energize solenoids, and segments of circuits to activate or stop the various components in the system.

Most machines offer a choice of fill levels—high, medium, or low—depending on the amount of wash to be done. When the user makes a fill selection, a pressure switch or a float switch is preset to open when the proper level is reached. In the same manner, selecting hot, warm, or cold wash water involves opening or closing the water inlet valves by means of solenoids.

The fill switch in most machines is in control throughout the operation. With the fill switch in control, the agitator cannot function until the machine is filled with water to the proper level. Initially, then, when the user pushes the start button, the water-pump inlet valve is opened and water is admitted into the machine. If the user selects a hot wash cycle, a solenoid is energized to open the hot water inlet, bypassing the cold water solenoid valve, or vice versa, for a cold wash. If a warm wash had been selected, both solenoids would have been energized. The water is cut off by the pressure or float switch when the proper level is reached.

In the meantime, the timer motor has been slowly revolving, rotating the cam wheels until finally a switch closes that completes the circuit to the transmission. The fill switch is still in control, however, and will not permit current to flow to energize the transmission until fill has been achieved.

When the fill switch has been satisfied, current to the transmission now flows and another solenoid is energized. This solenoid, through mechanical means which will be examined later, causes the drive clutch to engage and the agitator begins to oscillate, or the tumbler basket begins to revolve, in the wash cycle.

Agitators as well as the cylinder basket in tumbler washers are driven through either a gear train or a clutch arrangement. In the case of an agitator, it is driven by means of either (1) a train consisting of a pinion gear, a drive gear, a connecting rod, and a sector gear, or (2) a rack and pinion arrangement. These mechanical assemblies serve to convert the rotary motion of the drive motor to an oscillating motion, driving the agitator through an arc of about 180° at 60 strokes per minute. In some agitator washers, the cylinder basket may wobble slightly during agitation, but it does not spin. However, during the spin cycle, the agitator is locked in with the cylinder basket so that both are turning. If the agitator did not turn during spin, the clothes would be torn between the spinning basket and the stationary agitator.

After the agitation or wash cycle, a cam surface on the timer-motor cam assembly closes another switch, energizing a solenoid valve to open and drain the tub. In most washers, the water pump is constantly in operation during the entire wash and spin cycle so that it is only necessary to open and close various valves in the water system to achieve fill, drain, and spray rinses. During drain, all motion of the agitator or cylinder basket stops under the control of the fill switch, which will not permit resumption of drive until all the water is emptied from the tub.

A short spin cycle may follow, designed to remove any suds that may remain in the tub and the clothes. A spray rinse, in which a small amount of water is admitted briefly into the tub, helps this cycle along. During the spray cycle, the outlet valve remains open so that the water which is admitted drains out immediately.

The timer motor now advances another cam surface to close the switch controlling the water-inlet valve, at the same time opening the circuit to the drive solenoid, causing the cylinder basket to come to a stop. After a brief pause, the timer motor closes the fill switch and the tub fills with water again. In some washers, this fill temperature may be preselected at the start from a dial which affords various combinations of hot, warm or cold wash, and warm or cold rinses.

The deep-rinsing cycle is usually brief, accompanied by a short period of agitation. At its conclusion, all motion of the cylinder basket or agitator again comes to a stop and the tub empties.

The washer now goes into the final rinse and spin-dry cycles. Final rinsing may consist of a spin, accompanied by one or two brief spray rinses, the purpose of which is to dislodge, through the holes in the cylinder basket, any residue of soap scum or dirt which may have been deposited on the surface of the clothes as the water level receded during the drain cycle. After the last spray rinse, the cylinder basket continues to spin at high speed for a few minutes, during which most of the water is driven out of the clothes by the centrifugal force of the spin.

Finally, the timer motor advances to a point where all circuits are opened and the washer shuts itself off.

CONVENTIONAL WASHERS

Conventional washers are relatively simple in operation (Fig. 3-5). The user fills the tub by means of a hose

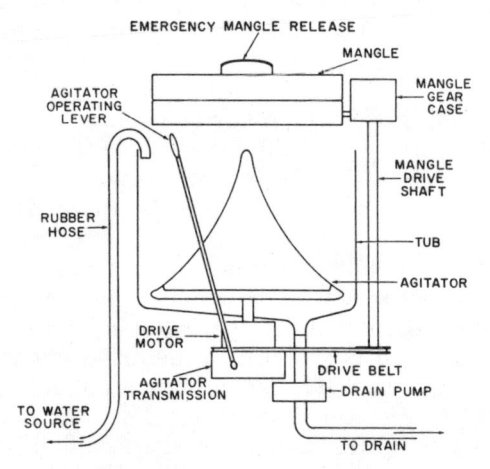

Fig. 3-5. Pictorial diagram of a conventional washer.

connected to a nearby mixing faucet, soap and bleach are added, and the washer motor is turned on. The user starts agitation by throwing a clutch lever which engages a gear train similar to that used in an automatic washer. The agitator operates with an oscillating motion until the user decides the clothes have been washed long enough. The agitator clutch lever is then disengaged and the hand-operated drain valve turned to Drain.

It is important to understand the need for the agitator to stop during drain. If it were to continue operating without water in the tub, it would be many times more difficult to push against the weight of the clothes, probably causing a motor overload. In addition, the clothes themselves might become mangled in the process.

Draining is accomplished in a conventional washer either by gravity (permitting the water to flow down through the drain hose into a drain in the floor of the laundry room), or by means of a water pump. The pump operates continuously as long as the motor is turned on, the user accomplishing draining by opening a valve in the pump. The tub is then refilled with clear water for a deep rinse, also accompanied by agitation.

In a wringer washer the mangle is turned on by means of a lever. This engages a vertical shaft which transfers power from the drive motor to the mangle gear train and rollers. The rollers of the mangle are made of soft rubber or composition and are adjustable by means of a pressure-regulating knob.

In twin-tub conventional washers (Fig. 3-6), the user places the damp clothes in a spin basket, which is caused to rotate at high speed by engaging another clutch lever. Most twin-tub washers, however, have a basket of relatively small diameter, necessitating a much higher rate of spin than the larger diameter basket of an automatic washer. Some of the older models of twin-tub washers have no safety switch to stop the spin basket when the access door is opened. All later models do have some such device, as well as a braking mechanism to bring the spinning basket to a stop as quickly as possible.

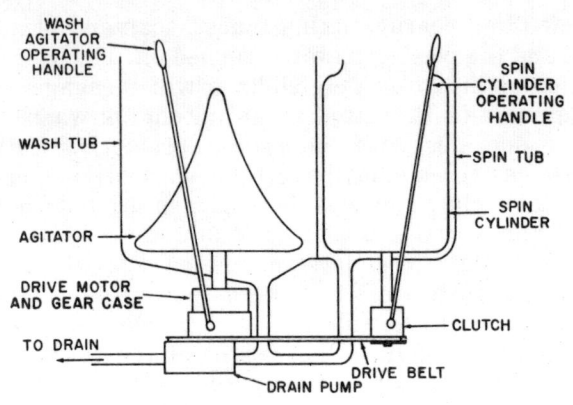

Fig. 3-6. Twin-tub washer.

MECHANICAL SYSTEMS

In this group of components are found the main-drive motor, the gear-train assembly which powers the agitator in agitator washers, and the basket-drive and brake assembly which drives the basket in both agitator and tumbler washers.

Gear Train

As mentioned previously, gear trains in agitator washers may be of either the sector gear, connector rod, or the rack and pinion gear type.

In the rack and pinion type (Fig. 3-7), a drive gear is driven by the main belt, taking power from the motor.

A stud mounted on the drive gear provides a bearing surface for a connecting rod, which is machined at its

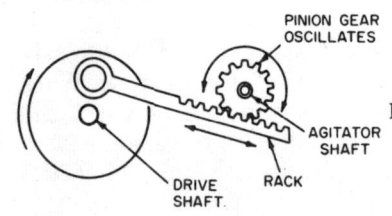

Fig. 3-7. Rack-and-pinion drive.

other end with a row of gear teeth, called a *rack*. As the main-drive gear rotates, the connecting rod is moved back and forth at about 60 complete strokes per minute. The rack end of the connecting rod meshes with the teeth on the pinion gear which is fixed to the agitator shaft, thus imparting an oscillating motion to the agitator. The latter travels approximately 180°, first in one direction, then the other, also at approximately 60 complete movements per minute.

In a variation of this method, a sector gear (Fig. 3-8) is employed in place of the rack gear. A pinion gear drives

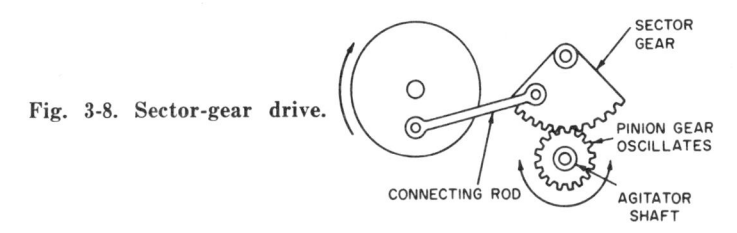

Fig. 3-8. Sector-gear drive.

a larger main-drive gear as in the previous example. A connecting rod is attached, through bearing surfaces on both ends, to the main-drive gear and a sector gear, the latter pivoting on a stud through a 180° arc. The sector gear meshes with the agitator gear to accomplish oscillation.

In both methods the drive belt is operating continuously as long as the motor is turned on, which means that the agitator would oscillate continuously if some method were not introduced to disengage the gear train at the appropriate points in the washing cycle. This is accomplished by converting the electrical impulse of a solenoid plunger into mechanical action.

It is important to understand that the amount of force exerted by a solenoid plunger would never, of itself, be sufficient to disengage the gear train of a mechanical system powered by a ⅓ or ½ hp motor. Some other means of actually extracting a gear from the train must be used. Thus, the extraction is initiated but not actually accom-

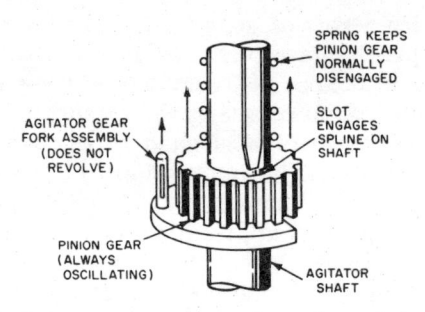

Fig. 3-9. Agitator gear mounted on the agitator shaft.

plished by the solenoid plunger. Here's how one such system works:

The location chosen for the breaking of the gear train is the meeting of the rack or sector gear with the agitator shaft. This provides the greatest amount of cushioning for the sudden shock of the meshing of the gear teeth.

The agitator gear may be moved to one of two positions on the agitator shaft (Fig. 3-9). In its upper position it locks with the shaft by means of a pin. A spring exerts pressure downward, keeping the gear from locking with the agitator shaft. In its lower position, the agitator gear oscillates freely, entirely independent of the agitator.

A solenoid assembly is mounted on the shaft of the sector gear (Fig. 3-10) or connecting rod rack so that the

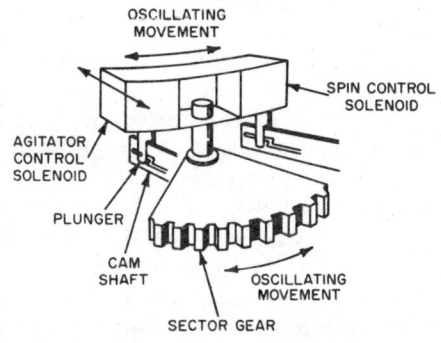

Fig. 3-10. Solenoid assembly rides on the sector-gear shaft.

entire solenoid assembly rocks back and forth with it. A cam bar is mounted between the solenoid assembly and the agitator gear. The plunger of the solenoid normally stays down of its own weight. The lower end of the plunger is slotted so that the plunger straddles the cam bar, and a horizontal pin is fitted to the ends of the fork formed by the slot in the plunger, passing through a two-level slot in the cam bar (Fig. 3-11). Normally, the plunger rides in the lower level of the slot, carried there by its own weight.

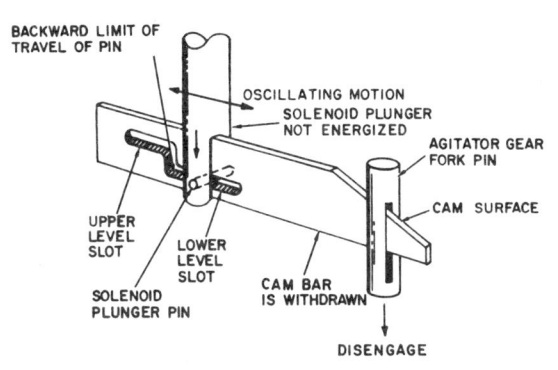

Fig. 3-11. Solenoid plunger detail (not actuated).

The lower slot on the cam bar is so located that the rocking (lateral) action of the solenoid assembly riding on the sector gear will maintain the cam bar in the withdrawn, or back, position of its lateral travel.

As soon as the solenoid is energized, however, it pulls the plunger upward. On the next rocking motion the plunger is pulled up into the upper level of the cam-bar slot (Fig. 3-12). This slot is so located that the rocking action (powered by the drive motor, not by the solenoid coil) will push the cam bar forward. A cam surface at the agitator gear end of the cam bar causes the agitator gear fork to travel upward, taking the agitator gear with it. The latter now engages with the pin in the agitator drive shaft, and the agitator begins to oscillate.

When the solenoid circuit is opened, the plunger will fall of its own weight, dropping to the lower level of the slot on the cam bar and thus withdrawing the front end of the cam bar from the agitator fork. This permits the spring on the agitator shaft to force the agitator gear downward to disengage it.

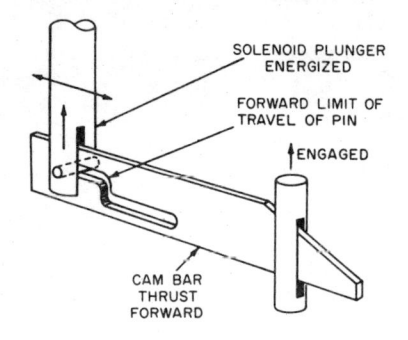

Fig. 3-12. Solenoid plunger energized.

Basket-Drive and Brake Assembly

In both agitator- and tumbler-type washers, the cylinder basket is driven by a V-belt riding on a drive pulley. In agitator washers the same belt drives both the basket and pinion gear pulleys.

In tumbler washers it is necessary to reduce the speed of the cylinder basket from approximately 600 rpm in the spin cycle to the 50 or 60 rpm required in the wash cycle. This is accomplished by a transmission or speed-change unit, which is actuated by a solenoid plunger in much the same manner as described in the section on the agitator gear train.

A cylinder basket loaded with wet clothes and spinning at 600 rpm develops many hundreds of pounds of inertial force. This force not only is dangerous, but tends to keep the cylinder basket spinning for a very long time after the driving force is removed. Some sort of braking system is therefore required, for reasons of both safety and efficiency.

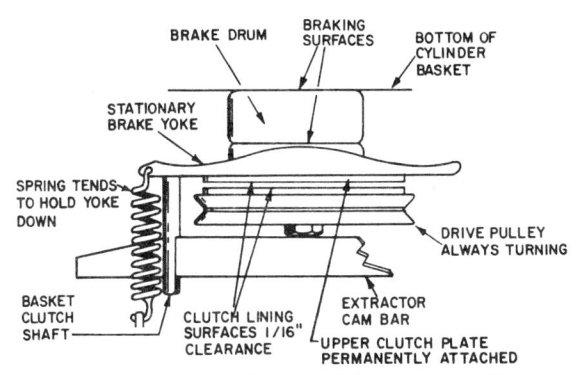

Fig. 3-13. Basket-drive and brake assembly.

A typical basket drive and brake assembly for an agitator washer is pictured in Fig. 3-13. For this type washer the agitator shaft passes through a drive tube, on which the cylinder basket is force-fitted. When the drive tube rotates, the cylinder basket rotates with it. The agitator shaft and the drive tube rotate independently of each other except during spin, when they are locked together as previously noted.

The basket-drive pulley is always turning whenever the drive motor is operating; it revolves freely on the drive tube. Directly above the basket-drive pulley is a basket-drive clutch disc which is permanently attached to the drive tube and is positioned to narrowly miss contact with a special clutch lining mounted on the top of the basket-drive pulley. Above the clutch disc is mounted the stationary brake yoke. A tension spring tends to pull the brake yoke downward, exerting pressure against the clutch disc, tending to cause it to engage the clutch lining on the basket drive pulley. This engagement is prevented, however, by a basket clutch shaft riding on the top edge of an extractor cam bar, which is normally thrust forward into a slot in the clutch shaft.

Above the brake yoke is mounted a brake-drum assembly, which is normally pressed against brake linings on both the bottom of the tub and the top of the brake yoke.

61

A solenoid assembly is mounted on the pivot stud of the sector gear, exactly the same as in the previous gear train discussion. As long as the solenoid is not energized, the plunger pin rides in the lower level of the extractor cam bar, allowing it to remain thrust forward into and holding up the basket clutch shaft.

When the solenoid is energized, the plunger is pulled upward by the magnetic force of the coil, and the pin now rides back and forth in the upper slot of the extractor cam bar. In so doing, it pulls the extractor cam bar backward out of the slot in the basket clutch shaft, allowing the latter to slide downward on the inclined cam surface of the bar toward the clutch lining.

The tension spring now forces the brake yoke downward, pressing the basket-drive clutch disc against the clutch lining on the top of the basket-drive pulley. After an initial slippage, the clutch lining firmly engages the basket-drive clutch disc (permanently attached to the basket-drive tube) and the cylinder basket begins to rotate. The basket gradually builds up speed until there is no longer any slippage, and the full speed and power of the motor are transmitted to the basket for the duration of the spin cycle.

When the solenoid is de-energized (either by opening the loading door or at the end of the spin cycle) the plunger drops down into the lower-level slot of the extractor cam bar. This pushes the front end of the bar into the basket clutch shaft and forces the brake yoke upward against the force of the tension spring to disengage the clutch from the clutch lining. As the brake yoke is forced upward, it closes the distance between the brake drums and the brake linings, bringing the heavily loaded basket to a quick, smooth stop.

Mangle

The mangle, or wringer (Fig. 3-14), of a conventional washer is an assembly designed to wring out moisture from the wet clothes when they are passed between two rubber or composition rollers under controlled pressure.

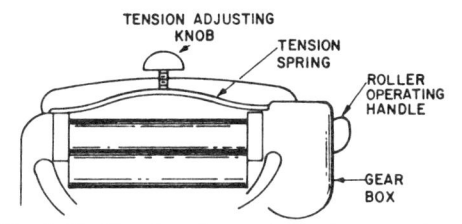

Fig. 3-14. Mangle of a wringer-type washer.

Power for the wringer is taken from the drive motor through a wringer-drive shaft (Fig. 3-15) turning a system of gears at the lower roller. The upper roller idles in most machines. A lever engages the gear train to operate the rollers, and generally affords three positions—forward, reverse, and stop.

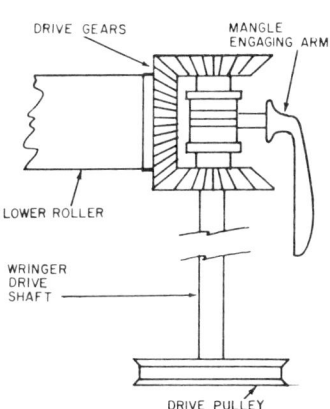

Fig. 3-15. Wringer power take-off.

THE WATER SYSTEM

The water system in an automatic washer (Fig. 3-16) consists of a series of valves, a water pump, and various accessory components such as dispensers, filters, hoses, etc.

Water enters the tub through an inlet valve, which may or may not provide an automatic temperature control for mixing hot and cold water. Usually, water enters the machine under its own pressure. As the water level rises, it actuates the fill switch, closing the circuit to the agitator control solenoid, and the machine begins the wash cycle.

In some machines, the water pump also serves to recirculate the water, taking it from the bottom of the tub and forcing it out through an inlet above the water level near the top of the tub. This recirculation serves to ensure that soaps and bleach are thoroughly mixed with the wash water. Energizing a solenoid on the water pump permits the passage of the recirculated water driven by the recirculating impeller.

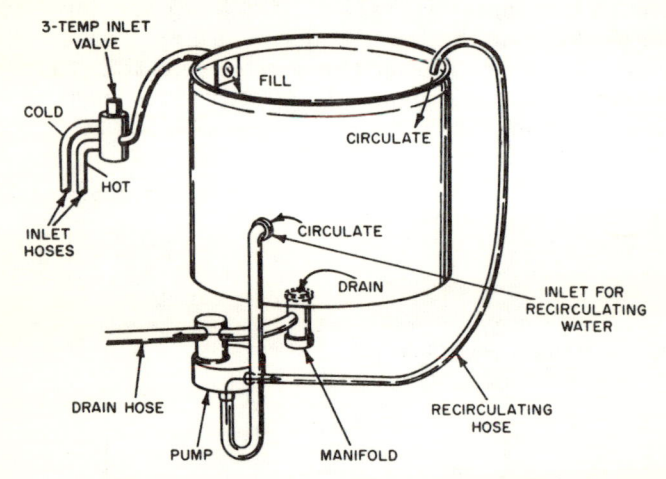

Fig. 3-16. Automatic-washer water system.

Water is ejected from the tub by the discharge impeller of the water pump. Discharge is effected by flapper valves in the body of the pump, which are actuated by the same mechanism that motivates the gear extraction in the drive.

Valves

The inlet valves of an automatic washer are operated by solenoid coils and plungers to permit or obstruct the passage of water. There are three basic types.

Single Solenoid Shutoff Valve (Fig. 3-17)—In this type, the solenoid performs only the function of shutoff, the

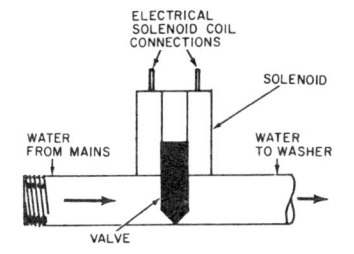

Fig. 3-17. Solenoid off-on valve.

mixing of incoming hot and cold water for desired wash and rinse temperature being performed at the faucets by the user.

Double Solenoid Shutoff Valve (Fig. 3-18)—This type of valve permits three water temperature selections—hot, warm, and cold. Energizing of the cold-water solenoid permits the passage of cold water only; energizing the hot-water solenoid allows only hot water to enter. When both solenoids are energized, both hot and cold water are admitted to the tub, resulting in a warm wash.

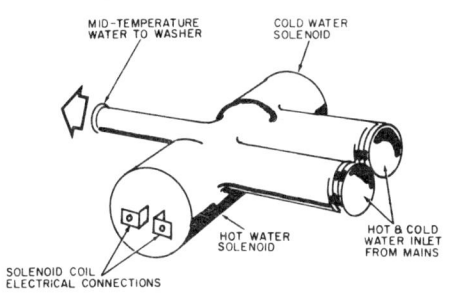

Fig. 3-18. Double-solenoid shutoff valve.

Triple Solenoid Shutoff Valve (Fig. 3-19)—This valve permits four different wash temperatures—hot, medium, warm, and cold. It has a mixing chamber in which cold and hot water in varying amounts are combined to obtain the desired wash temperatures.

The actual temperature of the wash water depends on the temperature of the water in the hot-water tank and the temperature of the cold tap water. In a double-solenoid

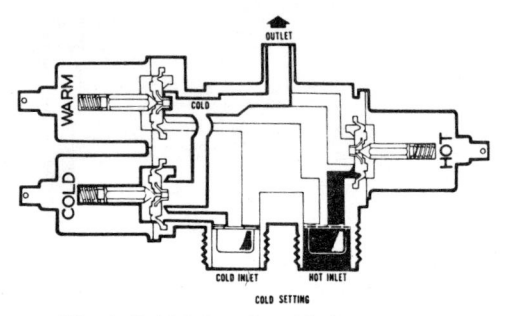

Fig. 3-19. Triple-solenoid shutoff valve.

inlet valve, the temperature of a warm wash will be equivalent to half the difference between tank water temperature and cold tap water temperature. For example, if tank temperature is 160°F., and the cold tap water is 50°F., the temperature of the water in a warm wash will be 105°F.

Two-Way Valves (Fig. 3-20)—Some washing machines employ a "suds-return" system whereby the sudsy water from the first wash is stored in one of a pair of dual laundry tubs and is used again in a subsequent wash. If the user selects the suds-return cycle, a solenoid is energized on the two-way valve to divert the drain water into the laundry tub instead of into the regular drain tub.

The solenoid is a "T" type, with a rubber diaphragm stretched over two ports. Energizing of the solenoid pulls

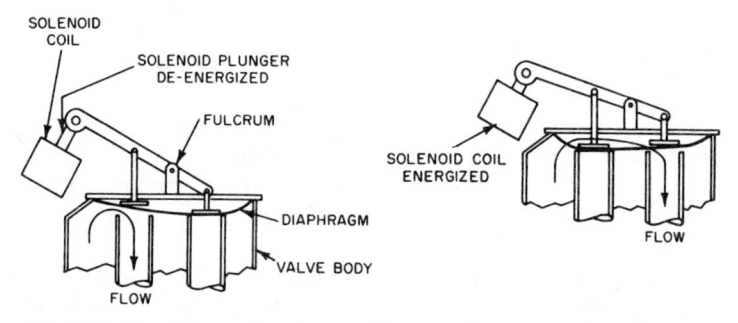

Fig. 3-20. Two-way suds-return valve permits reuse of wash water.

66

down one end of a pivoted operating lever which presses a disc against the rubber diaphragm over the drain port, while the other end pulls a disc away from the rubber diaphragm over the suds-return port. Normally, this valve directs the water flow into the drain port. Only sudsy water is stored in this system—rinse water is drained in the normal manner.

Water Pumps

The water pump (Fig. 3-21) operates continuously, receiving its power directly from the main drive belt. Most modern washers make use of a single-direction pump, meaning that the pump impeller rotates in only one

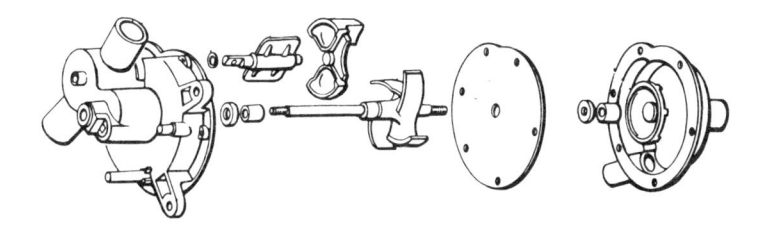

Fig. 3-21. Automatic washer water pump.

direction for both discharge and recirculation. The recirculating impeller and the discharge impeller are located at opposite ends of the impeller shaft which drives both. In the suds-return machine, the pump may also be used to return the sudsy water to the machine from the storage laundry tub.

Filters

Many different kinds of filters are employed in the different makes of washing machines. However, their main purpose is to strain out lint and other foreign particles which are loosened from the clothing by the agitating action. These filters are sometimes placed in the discharge line, and are removable for periodic cleaning. Other machines locate the filter in the recirculation system at the top of the tub. Still others may have filters located on the agitator.

Traps

Many washers are equipped with a trap assembly (Fig. 3-22). This serves to trap and hold any small objects which may otherwise circulate and damage the machine.

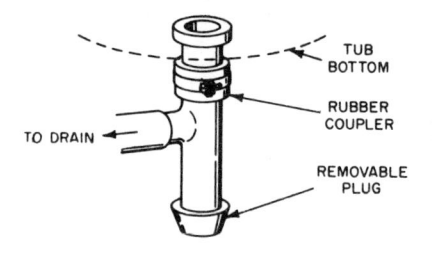

Fig. 3-22. Trap assembly.

THE ELECTRICAL SYSTEM

With the exception of the combination washer/dryer, automatic and conventional washers employ a 120-volt, 60-cycle a-c power source. Electricity is used to power not only the drive motor and the timer motor, but also the various electrical components used in controlling the flow of water in and out of the machine.

The following discussion of each of the common electrical components found in automatic washers will aid greatly in diagnosing and correcting electrical failures.

Timer

The timer (Fig. 3-23) is the heart of the control for all functions of an automatic washer. It consists of a synchronous motor (of the type usually found in clocks) which drives a pinion gear meshed with a drive gear in the timer assembly. This assembly may consist of a series of cam wheels or discs with inclined projections on their edges. As the cam wheels slowly revolve, cam surfaces rise to make contact with switch levers, which in turn open or close electrical circuits to solenoids in the mechanical system. The length of arc of each cam surface, as well as

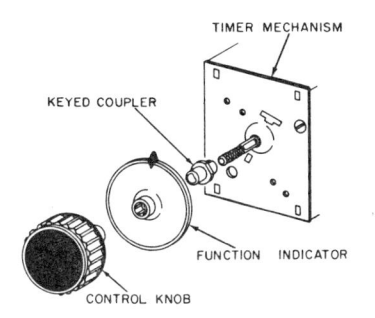

Fig. 3-23. Automatic-washer timer mechanism.

its position on the cam wheel with respect to other cams on the same and other wheels, is carefully planned so that the resulting action is accurately timed and synchronized.

Fill Switches

Fill switches are of two types—pressure-actuated and float-actuated. In a pressure-actuated switch (Fig. 3-24), a plastic tube of small diameter is connected to a standpipe, the opening of which is near the bottom of the washer tub. As the water level rises, a bubble of air is trapped in the plastic tub and compressed. A diaphragm in the switch body becomes distended as the air pressure

Fig. 3-24. Pressure switch used to control fill level.

69

in the tube builds up, and at a preselected pressure it causes a pair of electrical contacts to separate, opening the circuit to the inlet valve solenoid and cutting off the water supply.

A float switch is just what its name implies. A standpipe alongside the water tub fills with water to the same level as the water in the tub. A float rides up and down in this standpipe; as it reaches its upper limit, it trips an operating arm connected to a switch and opens the electrical circuit to the inlet-valve solenoid. As the water in the standpipe recedes, the weight of the float causes the switch to close so that water may be admitted when the timer completes the circuit.

Pressure switches are calibrated at the factory and the adjustment screw normally sealed against field adjustment. A very small movement of the screw would materially change the water level in the tub, requiring very painstaking accuracy. Defective pressure switches should be replaced, not repaired.

Fill switches, in addition to interrupting the current to the inlet-valve solenoids, are also in control of the other functions of the washer, since these other functions are dependent for their effectiveness on the proper water level (or absence of water) in the tub. When the fill switch is satisfied with respect to water level, it completes the circuits to the timer motor (the timer does not advance while the tub is filling initially) and to the solenoid in control of the agitator. In addition, the fill switch completes a circuit to the solenoid in control of the basket drive during the spin cycle. This latter circuit is completed when the pressure switch senses zero pressure, indicating that the tube is empty.

During the deep-rinse fill cycle, a bypass circuit passes control of agitation to the fill switch. This means that even if the cams in the timer advance to the point where agitation would normally begin, the fill switch would not permit the circuit to be closed. On the other hand, should fill be accomplished *before* the cams advance to the proper point, no agitation would take place until the timer circuits were completed. This delay until a stated time period elapses is necessary to compensate for the difference in faucet water pressures, which results in longer or shorter fill time.

Lid Switch

A switch connected between the spin solenoid and the timer is attached to the clothes-loading door or lid of most washers so that spinning stops when the door is opened. This is a safety measure added to prevent accidents.

Solenoids

Solenoids are a means of converting electrical energy into mechanical energy to trip switches, open and close valves, and actuate mechanical linkages. Solenoids consist of a coil of wire around which a magnetic field is developed when current passes through it. This relatively powerful magnetic force is able to move a metal core or plunger resting inside the coil. Various arrangements of plunger, core, and coil exist, but the resulting action is always the same. The movement of the plunger is resisted either by a spring or by gravity, so that when the energizing current is switched off, the plunger returns to its normal position.

Defective solenoids are usually replaced rather than repaired—especially water-valve solenoids, which are sealed at the factory to prevent the entry of water into their electrical components.

Drive Motor

The most popular type of motor used on washing machines is a ⅓ to ½ hp, 120-volt, 60-cycle, capacitor-start motor. It is equipped with thermal overload protectors which will disconnect the motor from the circuit if an overload condition occurs. These protectors reset themselves when the motor has cooled sufficiently, and operation can resume. However, if the condition which originally caused the overload is not corrected, the overload protector will soon open the motor circuit again.

In washers equipped with a selection of two speeds, the drive motor is provided with two run windings. The wiring harness is connected to three terminals at the motor; these terminals permit selections such as Normal Action or Gentle Action to bring one or the other run winding into operation to achieve different speeds.

Electrical Connections

Modern homes will have a convenient, grounded electrical outlet near the wash tubs. Some of these outlets are equipped with a three-prong receptacle to accept the three-pronged plug of the washer, the third prong being connected to the ground. Be sure the receptacle is actually grounded by testing as follows: Insert one probe of a tester in one hole of the outlet and touch the other to the cover-plate screw. If a test lamp, it should light; if a voltmeter it should read the full power-line voltage.

If the outlet is not grounded it will be necessary to run the ground wire provided by the manufacturer to the nearest cold water pipe. When this type of ground is used, the three-pronged plug may be used with a two-prong outlet by employing a special adapter. Local electrical codes will determine the advisability of using these adapters.

Electric combination washer/dryers will require a 240-volt power source in addition to the 120-volt source. These models are provided with a three-wire terminal block for convenience in making connections.

Gas combination washer/dryers will require plumbing connections to the gas supply pipe. It is a good idea when making this connection to provide an individual shutoff valve to the machine so that it may be isolated from the rest of the gas system whenever servicing is necessary. Joints must be carefully sealed to prevent the escape of even the smallest amount of gas. While a small gas leak may not constitute a serious threat to safety, it will be the source of a persistent odor. Test for leaks with soap bubbles. **Never test for inflammable gas leaks with an open flame!**

All combination units will require some means of venting to the outdoors (except those provided with a condenser lint trap). For venting suggestions, see the discussion in Chapter 4.

PERFORMANCE CHECKS

Checking the performance of a washer to pinpoint the cause of failures requires checking a particular component at the time in the wash or rinse cycle at which it is *supposed* to operate. For example, if the inlet-valve solenoid is suspected of failure, the washer timer dial should be turned to the initial fill position, so that the electrical circuit to the solenoid is completed. Only then is it possible to test for continuity in the circuit. Similarly, if the agitator cam solenoid is suspected, the timer dial should be advanced to the wash cycle to complete the circuit to the agitator solenoid.

Common Failures and Replacements

Among the more common failures requiring replacement in automatic washers are:

Worn or Broken Drive Belt—A loose belt is betrayed by a flapping noise throughout the cycling of the washer, and particularly when the machine is agitating or spinning. A broken belt, of course, results in no agitation, spin, or pumping, although initial fill will take place as usual. Replacement of the belt usually involves very little more than just slipping the new one over the motor pulley and the various drive pulleys, and adjusting tension. Tension adjustment is usually accomplished at the motor, by means of a slotted hole through which passes a motor mount bolt. Simply loosen the mounting bolt, and pivot the entire motor until the proper tension is achieved. Drive belts should be tight enough to form a straight line between the pulleys, but not so tight that they cannot be flexed for an inch or two at the midway point between.

Defective Timer Assembly or Motor—Timer assemblies are susceptible to wear because of their relatively fragile construction. Faulty timers may be detected by erratic functioning of the washer. Most timer trouble occurs at the switches, where burnouts, corrosion, and film deposits may cause open circuits or shorts. Normally, it is far easier and cheaper to replace a timer assembly than to attempt to repair it. The installation of a pushbutton timer requires synchronizing and indexing. Replacement timers are accompanied by detailed instructions for installation.

Pressure and Float Fill Switches—Defective fill switches will be evidenced by incorrect water levels or by overflowing of the tub. Float switches, unless the standpipe is protected with a screen, are likely to become stuck by the introduction of small objects.

Control Solenoids—In most cases, these will also fail due to a fault in the electrical components, rather than their mechanical elements. Check for continuity by placing a test lamp in series with the solenoid terminals. Faulty solenoids are detected by noting the absence of a particular function when it should occur, such as agitation, spin, or fill.

Drive Motor—The first check of a drive motor is to see if it is receiving the proper voltage. This is done by disconnecting the leads to the motor and connecting them to a voltmeter. If the proper voltage is recorded when the timer dial is turned to ON, the motor should be replaced. However, replacing the motor will certainly not eradicate the basic cause for the failure. Remember, motor burnouts don't just happen—they are caused. Here are some possible causes:

1. Extremely low-voltage conditions.
2. Loose electrical connections.
3. Binding in the motor bearings or the washer mechanism, or foreign particles in the motor switch.
4. Overload, evidenced by a high wattage reading.

The following are some of the reasons for additional loads on the motor:

1. Pump clogged with foreign material, or impeller shaft binding.
2. Lack of lubrication at bearing surfaces or in gear case.
3. Drive belt bottoming in pulleys. Belts are intended to seat in pulleys so their outer edges are slightly higher than the edge of the pulley. *Bottoming* means that too much belt surface is coming in contact with the pulley, resulting in a drag. When belt is found to be bottoming, replace. Too tight an adjustment of the drive belt can also cause the same condition.

Too slow spinning may, of course, be due to binding in the mechanical train. However, it must be borne in mind that slow spinning can also be caused by belt slippage, which is in turn caused by oil or grease on the belt. The basket-drive clutch plate may also become fouled with oil, requiring cleaning or replacement.

TROUBLESHOOTING GUIDE

The following is a list of some of the more common failures, along with possible causes and their solutions.

No Water to Machine

1. Water faucets closed (it does happen).
2. Faulty inlet valve solenoid. If the hot water selection is made on a dial, and either the switch or the solenoid on the hot-water inlet valve is defective, water will not enter the machine, since the cold-water line is closed. Check continuity in the switch and solenoid and replace if either shows an open.
3. Open timer circuit. Replace timer assembly.
4. Open wiring harness circuit. Check between electrical components for continuity. Repair or replace broken wires.
5. Clogged inlet valve screen. Remove and clean screen. Be careful not to bend or distort the screen surface when performing this operation.
6. Defective water-level float or pressure fill switch.

Check for electrical continuity and mechanical operation. Repair or replace as necessary.
7. Miscellaneous causes such as loose leads on electrical components, kinked hoses, trouble in the house water supply, etc. Make visual check to spot and correct trouble.

Motor Will Not Run

1. Branch-line fuse blown or circuit breaker tripped. Replace or reset. Fuse may blow as a result of a temporary overload when two or more appliances start up at the same time. Check to determine whether branch line is carrying too many amperes. Relocate appliances on different branch lines if necessary.
2. Overload protector tripped due to a thermal overload. Wait for thermal discs to cool, and then try motor again. If overload trips again, search elsewhere for overload condition.
3. No power to washer. Plug voltmeter into machine, and line cord into voltmeter, to check for line voltage. Replace line cord if indicated.
4. Inoperative motor. Disconnect leads to motor and connect them to voltmeter. If voltage registers, motor replacement is indicated.
5. Loose or disconnected leads to timer terminal block, etc. Tighten or make connections. Check all wiring.
6. Defective fill switch. Check and replace, if necessary.

Machine Will Not Agitate

1. Defective timer assembly. Check all leads for continuity. If no continuity exists between the common terminal and one or more of the other terminals in the assembly, timer must be replaced. If timer has separate motor which checks good, this part need not be replaced.
2. Faulty transmission. Make wattage test. If all other electrical tests are positive and wattage consumption is excessive, a mechanical fault in the drive mech-

anism is indicated. Transmissions of most washers may be repaired in the shop, first cleaning all parts to permit a careful visual check. It is not necessary to replace all the parts in the gear case—individual parts may be ordered by number by consulting manufacturers' literature. Check transmission parts for scoring, burrs, excessive wear, broken teeth and shafts, and broken or worn seals or gaskets.
3. Defective agitator solenoid. Check for continuity, mechanical freedom of movement of plunger, burrs on cam surfaces, slots, etc. Replace electrically defective solenoids, repair or replace mechanical parts as needed.
4. Inoperative motor, loose pulleys, defective fill switch, loose or disconnected leads, broken wiring, inoperative motor centrifugal switch. Take necessary action as indicated.

No Drain

1. Clogged drain pump or drain connections, loose or broken pump-impeller shaft, faulty flapper valves in pump. Low wattage with pump operating and water tub filled will indicate a broken impeller shaft. High wattage will indicate an obstruction in the pump or connections. Repair or replace as indicated.
2. Kinked drain hose, air lock, or suds lock. Air lock may be caused by baffle missing on tub at drain port. Suds lock is caused by excessive suds. Add cold water to tub and scoop out suds.

No Spin

1. Loose or broken belt. Inspect and replace or adjust. Grease or oil on clutch plate or on drive belt will result in slow spin, or no spin.
2. Faulty lid switch. Check for continuity with lid lowered. If no continuity, replace switch.
3. Defective spin solenoid. Check for continuity; replace if necessary. Check mechanical train triggered by solenoid for burrs, bent cams, etc.

4. Faulty water-level switch, broken wires, loose lead connections.

Excessive Vibration

1. Some washers have an unbalanced load cut-off switch which will stop the washer if an excessively unbalanced load occurs. In other machines, the washer may "walk" with an unbalanced load. Correct the walking by adjusting and tightening the leveling legs. The walking condition may also be caused by sympathetic vibrations being set up in a weakened floor. Correct the floor condition.
2. Damaged or misadjusted suspension system. Check to make sure that all suspension rods, motor mounts, rubber blocks, etc., are equally tight. Also check any gear-case braces or brackets that may have come loose.

Torn Clothes

1. Broken agitator, or burrs on clothes basket. Inspect and replace, if necessary.
2. Overloading and the excessive use of bleach can cause damage to clothes. Check operating instructions.

Water or Machine Will Not Shut Off

1. Defective inlet valve or fill switch will cause overflowing. If fill switch opens at proper level and water continues above prescribed water level, faulty inlet valve is indicated. Also check wiring harness, timer, motor centrifugal switch, solenoid on inlet valve, and hoses.

Water and Oil Leaks

1. Check inlet and drain hoses for tight connections; check pump gasket, gear-case gaskets and seals, tub gaskets and hose bodies for breaks.

CHAPTER 4

CLOTHES DRYERS

Clothes dryers accomplish drying by furnishing heated air in large volume into the interior of a rotating drum where the clothes are tumbled to expose all their surfaces to the passing air. Thus, a clothes dryer needs (1) a source of heat, (2) a means for tumbling the clothes, (3) a source for fresh air in large volume, and (4) a means of expelling moisture-laden air from the interior of the cabinet. In addition, dryers require controls for safeguarding clothes against extremes of heat and overdrying.

Fig. 4-1 is a block diagram which illustrates the operating pattern, as well as the general location, of the main components of a dryer. The relatively dry air from the surrounding room enters the dryer cabinet through various vents in the front and back. A blower system forces this air through a flue arrangement where it is heated and then into the revolving drum through holes in the front face.

The bulk of the air circulates freely in the interior of the drum, passing through the tumbling clothes. The air in the interior of the drum soon approaches saturation, absorbing moisture from the clothes. The blower, which operates continuously while the drum is in motion, forces the moisture-laden air out through a vent leading outside the cabinet. Most dryers require further venting to the outdoors.

The principle of operation of a dryer strikes a balance between two contributing factors. The first is that heated air can absorb more moisture than cool air. Air at 32°F. is capable of absorbing only about 2 grains of moisture per cubic foot. Air at 70°F. can absorb about 8 grains of moisture, while air heated to 160°F. absorbs 18.6 grains of moisture per cubic foot.

The second factor concerns the movement of air. Even if heated to 160°F., motionless air immediately adjacent to wet clothes will very quickly become saturated and

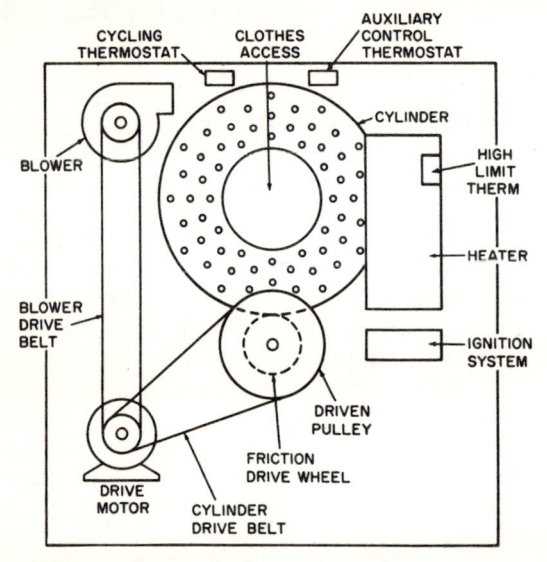

Fig. 4-1. Diagram of a modern clothes dryer.

unable to absorb any more moisture. If this air is replaced by currents of fresh, dry air, however, the moisture-absorbing process is hastened considerably.

By employing air that is both heated and moving (average temperature, 160°F., and moving at about 125-175 cfm) it is possible to hasten the natural drying process to a point where an efficient unit can remove approximately 10 lbs. of water (over 1 gal.) from a load of clothes in 1 hour. If the clothes are wrung out thoroughly before being placed in the dryer, a modern unit can dry a load of 19 or 20 lbs. (including the weight of the water) in about 1 hour.

GAS DRYERS

The controls and heater assembly (Fig. 4-2) of a gas dryer are far more complex than the comparable components in electric models because of the requirement of a pilot flame and the on and off cycling of the gas flow to the main burner.

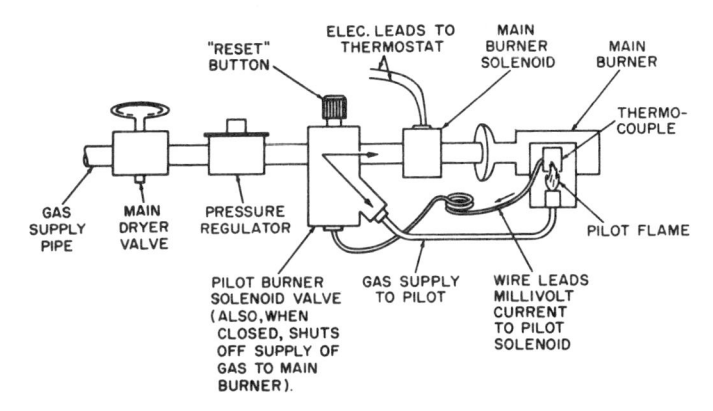

Fig. 4-2. Block diagram of gas controls.

Components

Following is a list of the main components of a typical gas dryer, with a description of their functioning.

Power-Cord Plugs—These are usually of the three-prong type, the third prong being a cabinet ground. Most appliances are provided with an alternate ground wire and harness for attaching to the nearest suitable ground. Local electrical codes will spell out whether or not adapters for wall outlets may be used along with the alternate ground harness.

Motors—Dryer motors are usually ¼- to ⅓-hp, 120-volt, 60-cycle, split-phase types of approximately 1725 rpm. Gas dryers, unlike electric, require only regular 120-volt house current for operation. A shaft protruding from both ends of the motor provides a power take-off for the revolving drum on one end and the blower on the other.

Main-Burner Gas Solenoids—These may be actuated by either 120- or 24-volt current, the latter being stepped down by a transformer. The gas solenoid (Fig. 4-3) is wired in series with the control thermostats and the cen-

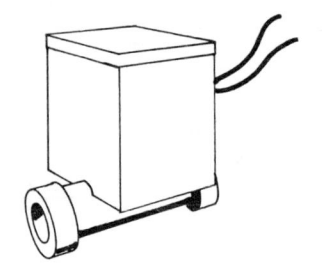

Fig. 4-3. Sketch of main-burner solenoid.

trifugal switch. The centrifugal switch is extra insurance against dangerous build-up of high heat, opening the main-burner valve only after the motor has attained run speed.

Timers—Timers may be driven by a spring-wound clock mechanism or by an electric motor (Fig. 4-4A). Fig. 4-4B shows the arrangement and method of operation of a typical cam used in these timer mechanisms.

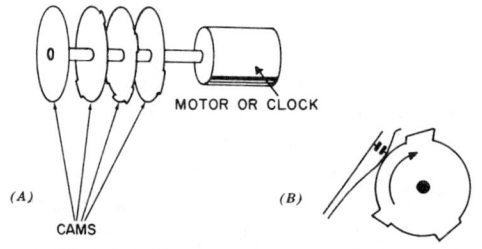

Fig. 4-4. Dryer cam-operated timer.

Automatic Controls—These controls for heavy and light loads, etc., are normally of the potentiometer type, permitting selection of various degrees of resistance ahead of the auxiliary control thermostat. By reducing or increas-

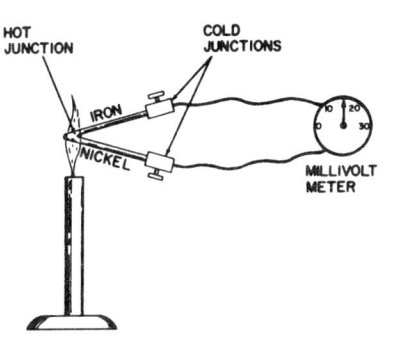

Fig. 4-5. A thermocouple.

ing amperage, the wattage consumption of the bias heater of the auxiliary control thermostat is carefully controlled, causing the auxiliary control thermostat to open later or sooner as a means of controlling the length of the heat-on cycle.

Thermocouples—When the pilot burner is lighted, a hot and cold junction of the two metals iron and nickel (Fig. 4-5) creates a current, measured in millivolts of electricity, in a coil around the solenoid valve plunger. The current is sufficient to hold open the plunger, though not sufficiently strong initially to overcome the force of a spring. Thus, it is necessary to press a button to hold the plunger open against the force of the spring until the thermocouple joint warms up sufficiently (about 20-30 seconds), after which the small thermocouple-generated current is sufficient to hold up the solenoid.

Any momentary interruption of this small current will cause the solenoid plunger to close the valve, shutting off the supply of gas to both the pilot and the main burner. This valve will not reopen by itself—the start button must be pressed again and a flame applied to the pilot burner.

"Spark Plugs" or Glow Coils—A 24-volt transformer supplies current to a 24/2.5-volt transformer which energizes a glow coil located at the pilot burner. The current causes the coil of platinum wire to give off an intense heat, sufficient to ignite the gas coming out of the pilot burner. Once ignited, the gas flame is directed against

a bimetal strip, which instantly snaps to the open position, interrupting the flow of current to the glow coil. The extremely low voltage is necessary because a higher potential would quickly burn out the fine platinum wire.

Pressure Regulators—These devices are for regulating the escape pressure of the gas entering the dryer and are normally preset at the factory for 3½" water-column pressure. Adjustments may be made, when necessary, by means of an adjusting screw. This should be done by a qualified technician, who would follow the instructions in the manufacturer's literature, using a manometer for precise measurement of the gas pressure.

Burner Orifices—Different types of gas (natural, manufactured, LP., etc.) require different orifices. Dryers shipped to areas using a particular type of gas normally have the proper orifice already installed. The wrong orifice will greatly affect the Btu heat input of the burner.

Main-Burner Solenoid Valve—These valves control the flow of gas to the main burner and are wired in series with and controlled by the auxiliary control and high-limit thermostats. If the contacts of either thermostat are in the open position, the flow of current to the normally closed solenoid will be interrupted. When the contacts of both thermostats are in their normally closed position, a flow of current creates a magnetic field around the solenoid plunger, causing it to react against the force of a spring to open the gas valve.

The pilot-burner solenoid valve is located ahead of (in terms of gas flow) the main-burner solenoid so that if the pilot flame should go out and the thermocouple current to the pilot solenoid valve is interrupted, both the main and pilot-burner gas supply will be shut off.

High-Limit Thermostats—The function of the high-limit thermostat is to interrupt the current to the heater should the temperature of the heater housing exceed a preset limit. In some models, the high-limit thermostat also shuts off power to the drive motor so that the dryer must be restarted. This is an extra insurance against overheating.

High-limit thermostats are usually preset at the factory, with no further adjustment possible. In gas models, the high limit is set at approximately 275°F.±7°F.

Cycling Thermostats—In automatic models, normally closed cycling thermostats are used in conjunction with auxiliary control thermostats having bias heaters. The automatic types are preset at lower cut-on and cut-off temperatures than the timer-model dryers. No adjustment of temperature range in the home is possible.

When in the closed position, cycling thermostats pass current directly to the main-burner solenoid. When in the open position, the current is diverted to the flow path in which the auxiliary control thermostat is located, opening the circuit to the main heater.

Auxiliary Control Thermostats—These are of two types —the standard bimetal, normally closed, disc type, and the bimetal, normally closed, disc type with built-in bias heater.

The function of the auxiliary control thermostat is to open the circuit to the heater when its high limit (usually 20° or 30° higher than the cycling thermostat) is reached. When its low limit is reached, it closes the circuit to the heater, "passing the ball" again to the cycling thermostat for another heat-on cycle.

In some auxiliary control thermostats, the high limit causes it to snap into a position that opens a relay circuit to the heater, but provides a second path to the drive motor for a short "cool-down" period. When the low limit is reached after the cool-down period, the contacts snap back into the already open relay circuit and the machine is completely shut off.

Cylinder-Drive Assemblies—To reduce the 1725 rpm achieved by the drive motor to the 50 rpm (approximately) at which the clothes drum must revolve, a speed reduction system is required. One such system is shown in Fig. 4-6, in which the motor pulley drives a driven pulley, which in turn drives the drum. In a variation of this method (Fig. 4-7), the motor pulley is connected to the drum through a jackshaft. The outside circumference

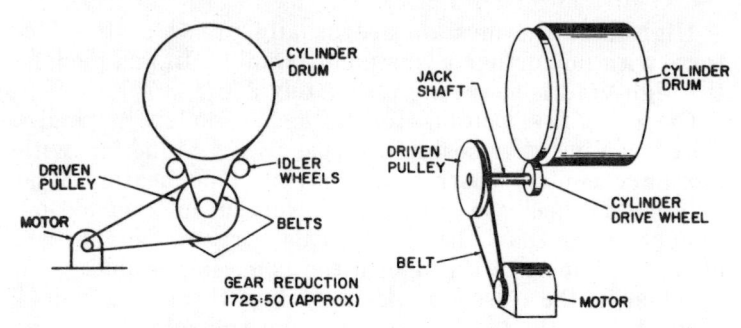

Fig. 4-6. Dryer cylinder-drive system.

Fig. 4-7. Friction cylinder-drive system.

of the drum's drive wheel is rubber, causing the drum to revolve by means of friction.

In earlier models, a belt switch is employed as a safety measure to protect against the dangerous build-up of heat should any of the belts break. The normally open switch (Fig. 4-8) is closed by a spring-loaded plunger which is kept in the closed position by the tension of the

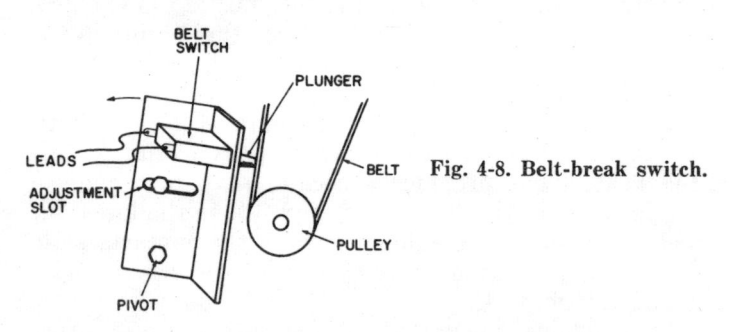

Fig. 4-8. Belt-break switch.

belt. If the tension should be relieved, as in the case of a broken or excessively loose belt, the spring forces the plunger to open the switch. This switch is connected in series with the main burner solenoid, thus shutting off the supply of gas.

The same protection is now afforded by the high-limit thermostat used in later models, which senses heat build-

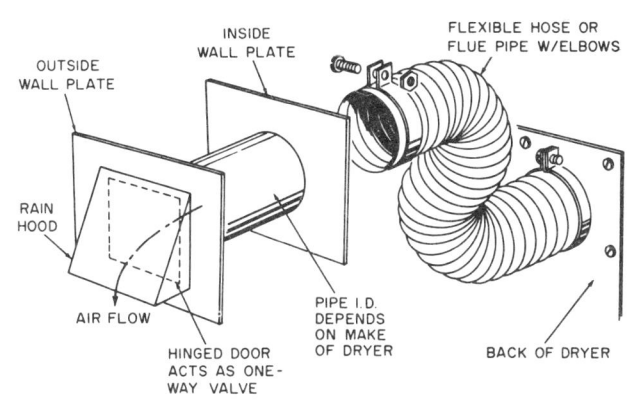

Fig. 4-9. Vent kit.

up and shuts off the main burner as well as the drive motor.

Clothes Doors—Most dryers employ a door switch which shuts off both heat and drive motor when the door is opened. In some models, the service door is also protected in the same manner.

Vent kits (Fig. 4-9) are available, for either a particular model, or universal types to fit all models. In venting to the outdoors, it is important that the dryer be located near an outside wall through which the vent pipe may be easily led. It is recommended that not more than four right-angle turns be made in the exhaust pipe, which may vary from 3 to 4 inches in diameter, depending on the dryer model. If four right angles are made in the exhaust pipe, not more than 20 ft. of straight pipe should be used to reach the outdoors. For two right angles, a maximum of 25 ft. of straight pipe may be used.

Some models of automatic dryers wash the lint produced by the dryer down the water drain. They accomplish this by passing the exhaust air through a condenser through which cold faucet water flows. As the air encounters the cold surfaces of the condenser, the moisture it contains condenses to liquid, carrying with it the tiny particles of lint that have escaped the lint filter. The condensate and the lint particles are washed down the drain by the same water that is used to cool the condenser.

ELECTRIC DRYERS

Electric dryers differ from gas models mainly in the source of heat, using an electrical heating element in place of the open gas flame. However, there are a few other differences.

The schematic diagram in Fig. 4-10 traces the circuitry of a typical electric dryer employing a timed drying cycle.

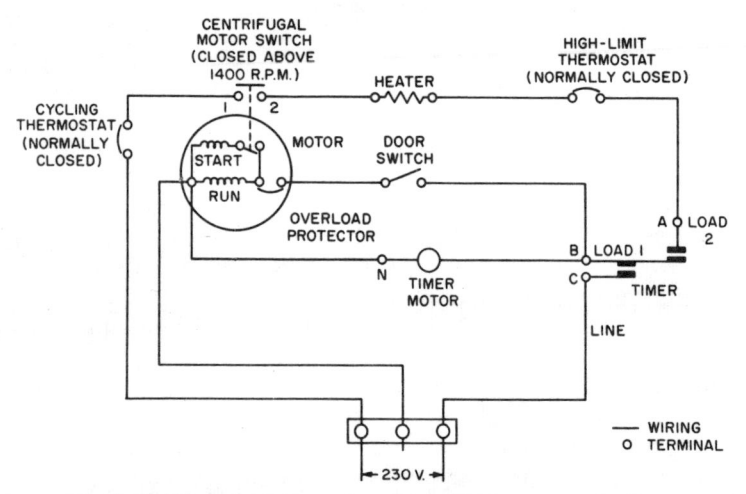

Fig. 4-10. Electric dryer schematic showing manual timer.

Note that the dryer requires a three-wire 240-volt power source for most efficient operation. It is possible to run the 240-volt heating element on standard 120-volt current by shifting one wire to the neutral line, as noted in Fig. 4-11, running only two wires to the power source. This, of course, cuts down the efficiency of the dryer by about half, which means that clothes will take twice as long to dry. It is not recommended practice.

A 240-volt dryer also requires a standard 120-volt circuit to drive the motor and the controls. This is obtained by using two of the three wires as shown in Fig. 4-11. Some electric dryers also make use of a 24-volt current, obtained by means of a transformer, to power the thermostat controls. A 24-volt current makes it possible to use less hefty components, thus cutting the costs of manufacture.

The heating element (Fig. 4-12) may be located in various places around the drum, the most widely used location being around the entire circumference at one edge. The element consists of a coil of wire through which

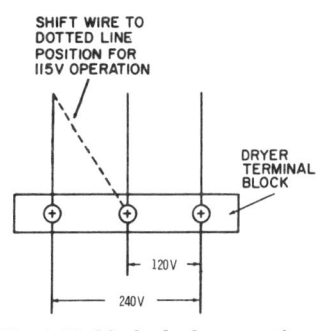

Fig. 4-11. Method of converting a 240-volt dryer to 120 volts.

Fig. 4-12. Heating element of a 240-volt dryer.

flows the 240-volt current. Most such heaters are rated at from 4000 to 5000 watts at 240 volts. The heater is mounted in such a position that the air entering the clothes drum must first pass over its coils. In electric dryers, the high-limit thermostat is located at or near the heater housing.

Repairs to the heater elements are not usually considered economically feasible. If an element fails, it is better to replace the entire heater assembly.

Fig. 4-13 shows a typical hook-up of an electric dryer. Note the use of No. 10 wire in the hook-up (if the dryer is located more than 60 feet from the main fuse box, use No. 8 wire). Electric dryers should be connected to a separate branch circuit with no other appliances on the same line. Fusing should be a minimum of 30 amperes.

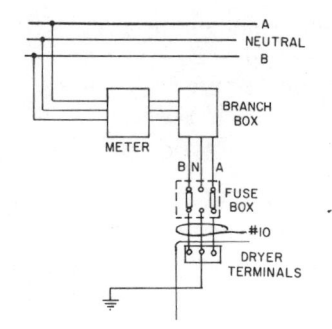

Fig. 4-13. Connection of a 240-volt dryer to the power source.

Performance Checks

Checking the performance of a dryer, apart from the obvious visual checks, is largely a matter of taking its pulse and temperature. Wattage readings, like pulse readings, will tell whether the components themselves are functioning properly. Temperatures at the exhaust air duct taken at the appropriate time in the drying cycle will give additional information which can be used to doublecheck the wattage findings.

An experienced technician relies heavily on the evidence of his senses in diagnosing trouble. He touches the air ducts to feel how hot they are; he looks for signs of wear on belts and other moving parts; he listens for telltale sounds that indicate some abnormal condition; he even smells for trouble such as gas leaks, heater and motor burnouts, etc. You should try to develop your senses, too.

All dryers employ essentially the same basic principle for their operation, as outlined at the beginning of this chapter. But different makes and models may differ very widely from each other in the details of horsepower, wattage, cut-out and cut-in temperatures, and air velocity, as well as types of timers, heaters, thermostats, regulators, valves, and other components. It would be quite beyond the scope of this book to attempt to define all the performance checks and ratings for each particular make and model.

However, the standards of performance of each dryer are usually published by the manufacturer in his service literature. This literature will list the actual rating figures for wattages, voltages, resistances, and temperatures. The following describes how these values are applied to the performance of the dryer being checked.

Temperature and Operating Check—If the dryer is a new installation, be sure to follow the manufacturer's instructions as to uncrating, removing shipping blocks, checking for loose wires, etc. Turn the unit on. If the dryer is run empty, add about 10°F.-15°F. to the values given in the manufacturer's ratings with full load.

Insert a thermometer (bimetal type, range 100° to 200°F.) in the exhaust air flow well inside the exhaust duct. Read temperatures during the heat-on cycle as well as during cool-down. When reading temperatures, use the highest reading during heat-on, the lowest reading during cool-down.

Readings of exhaust temperatures will be affected by the temperature of the room in which the dryer is located. Most performance standards take this into account, giving standard readings at different ambient temperatures.

Wattage Checks—Wattage checks are taken of the heater in electric dryers, as well as bias heaters in gas and electric auxiliary control thermostats. Wattage readings of the latter with a variance of 10% or more from the published standard indicate that replacement is required.

In addition, wattage readings may be taken of the drive motor under full or no load. Abnormally high wattage readings of the motor mean that (1) some abnormal binding condition exists in the cylinder drive system or the blower system, and (2) a serious obstruction exists in the air flow ducts.

Amperage Readings—To discover shorts in the wire harness, a fast, simple check may be made by using a hook-on ammeter (see Chapter 1).

Voltage Check—Particularly in electric dryers it is important that rated voltages be supplied to the dryer.

A 240-volt dryer will not operate as efficiently (resulting in slower drying) if the voltage supplied measures only 208 volts. Power supply voltages are read at the entrance to the dryer. If an exceptionally long lead is required from the power source to the dryer (60 ft. or more) the next larger size wire than that recommended by the manufacturer should be used.

Some manufacturers supply transformer kits to step up or step down voltage from 208-240 volts or 240-208 volts. These kits are generally accompanied by detailed installation instructions and a wiring diagram.

Common Failures and Replacements

Failures in dryers occur most often in the moving parts of the cylinder drive system. One of the most frequently encountered failures is a worn-out drive belt. Excessive belt wear may be caused by binding at the pulley bearing, or too much or too little belt tension. To correct or prevent binding conditions at the pulley be sure to lubricate it properly. See Chapter 1 for tips on lubrication.

Belt tension may be checked visually. The belt should be tight enough to form a straight line where it travels from one pulley to the next. It should not be so tight that you cannot flex it slightly at the midpoint between pulleys with a slight squeeze. Be careful not to get oil in the pulley grooves or on the belt itself when lubricating. Oil deteriorates rubber.

Another common failure in dryers is a motor burnout. However, motor burnouts don't just happen—they are caused. When replacing the motor of any appliance, look for a reason for the failure. Among the more common causes for a motor burnout are a defective overload protector, loose or shorted wiring in the appliance, as well as within the motor itself, binding in the moving parts, and fusing or house wiring defects. Be sure the branch-wire fuses or circuit breakers are of the proper rated amperage as given on the dryer nameplate.

A less frequent cause of trouble may be found in the venting system. An excessive amount of lint build-up will interfere with the free flow of air through the dryer. A dislocation of an air duct may cause the escape of lint to the moving parts of the dryer.

Venting systems have also been known to "blow back." Strong or gusty winds from the outdoors may enter the dryer through the exhaust vent outlet and actually blow out the pilot flame. The exhaust vent should be provided with a hinged aluminum door that will only permit the outward flow of air. Be sure the door moves freely under light pressure so the exhaust air flow will not be restricted.

Timer motors tend to fail after long use. Contacts may burn out, or internal circuitry may become shorted or leaky. Replacement of the entire component is usually the best course.

In gas dryers the most frequent cause for failure in the gas system is the pilot-burner solenoid valve.

TROUBLESHOOTING GUIDE

Before any repairs or disassembly is attempted on a dryer, the power cord should be pulled from the wall outlet—especially important in electric dryers, because of the high voltages developed and because dryers are frequently located on basement floors in direct contact with the ground. When checking components, such as heaters with the dryer partially disassembled, turn on the timer motor to the appropriate point in its cycle and then plug in the power cord without touching the cabinet or other components. Testing for shorts of individual components or wiring harness with an ohmmeter or test lamp may be accomplished in most cases without turning the dryer on.

Following are some of the more common signs of trouble in a dryer, both electric and gas, and the probable causes and remedies. It is by no means a complete list, but should serve as a guide to solve most of the problems encountered.

Dryer Does Not Start

1. Power failure. Look for blown fuse or circuit breaker, breaks in house wiring or power cord, or de-

fective power-cord plug. If the fuse is blown, look for underlying causes, such as high voltage, another appliance on the same branch line, etc. Merely replacing a fuse does not correct the cause of failure.
2. Defective motor, door switch, or timer motor. Apply test lamp to component leads to check for shorts. Press door switch button manually with dryer turned on to check for mechanical defect. Replace or repair as necessary.
3. Loose connections at components or terminal block. Check segments of wire circuitry with test lamp.
4. Inoperative or defective high-limit thermostat. Thermostat is normally closed, will permit current flow at temperatures below danger level. Test thermostat leads with ohmmeter or test lamp. If contacts are open at less than rated cut-out temperature, thermostat is defective and should be replaced.

Motor Runs But Drum Does Not Turn

1. Loose or broken drive belt; pulley loose on drive shaft. Make necessary repairs or replacements.

No Heat, Drum Turns

1. In electric dryers, look for defective circuitry at or near the heating element and within the heating element coil itself. Test for shorts with test lamp.
2. In gas dryers, look for a defective pilot-burner solenoid valve or a defective main-burner solenoid. These components are generally sealed and must be replaced as an assembly. Also check gas supply lines and main valve.
3. Check for a defective open or shorted cycling thermostat or auxiliary control thermostat. Manufacturer's literature will give the proper ranges of these thermostats, as well as approved test procedures for testing bias heaters in auxiliary control thermostats. The range of a thermostat may become disturbed without causing the thermostat contacts to test open

or short. If this is suspected, the thermostat should be replaced.
4. In earlier models, a worn or loose belt may cause the protective belt switch to function, shutting off the flow of current to the electric heater or to the main gas burner solenoid valve.

Dryer Will Not Shut Off

1. Inoperative or defective clock timer or timer motor. A bent stop pin on the timer dial may prevent the dial from rotating all the way to Stop. Burned out contacts in the timer may also cause this symptom. Check also for shorting of the timer internal circuitry as well as the drive motor.

Slow Drying

1. Improper loading. Overloading, or loading clothes into the dryer that are not thoroughly wrung out, will of course increase drying time.
2. Air flow restriction. Check ducts, lint traps, outdoor exhaust outlet. Check also for improper blower functioning, loose blower drive belt, worn out moving parts on blower, etc.
3. Cutout temperature may be too low. Make temperature check as given above. If cutout temperature is lower than minus tolerance given in manufacturer's literature, the cycling thermostat should be replaced, unless the range adjusting screw is accessible for field adjustment.
4. Low voltage (in electric dryers). Check voltage at power source and at the dryer terminals. If voltage drop is excessive (20 or more volts) replace branch line with next larger size wire. If voltage is low at power source, consult local utility.

Gas Pilot Flame Will Not Stay Lit

1. Check positioning of thermocouple joint in relation to pilot flame. One-half inch of tip of thermocouple should be buried in the flame, with the flame break-

ing around it. Adjust height of flame by turning pilot flame adjusting screw until flame burns blue without hissing noise.
2. Check circuitry from thermocouple to solenoid coil.

Gas Pilot Flame Will Not Light
1. Check gas supply and house gas valve as well as dryer main gas valve, and pilot-burner solenoid valve.
2. If glow coil is employed, check 24/2.5-volt circuit for breaks. Check visually for breaks in glow coil. Replace if necessary.

Gas Main Burner Will Not Light
1. Check main-burner solenoid valve and circuitry with test lamp for breaks or shorts in magnetic coil.
2. Check main-burner air shutter for clogging. Adjusting screw releases shutter so that it may be turned to admit more or less air until a clean-burning blue flame with a minimum of noise is achieved.